Overcoming
Apraxia

By Laura Baskall Smith

ISBN: 978-0-578-57537-7 (paperback)

To my husband, who has always been supportive and encouraged me to follow my dreams. To my two children, who are my light and my loves. The greatest privilege of my life has been in being your mom.

TABLE OF CONTENTS

INTRODUCTION

This book is for anyone who is interested in learning more about childhood apraxia of speech (CAS) from both a clinical standpoint and a personal one. Throughout this book the terms CAS and apraxia are used interchangeably but are both referring to apraxia that started in childhood. I was a speech-language pathologist (SLP) with some modest experience with CAS before the birth of my daughter. When she was nearly three years old, I learned that she had apraxia and my world turned upside down. After learning so much more about apraxia, I am now in private practice, specializing in the disorder.

Apraxia is a motor planning disorder that affects a child's ability to plan and program the precise movements needed for speech and results in difficulties producing and blending speech sounds smoothly and correctly. Speech therapy is needed to address this motor planning component. Therapy for apraxia can help other speech disorders; however, approaches that do not target the underlying speech motor difficulty are not likely to be effective for apraxia.

When a child isn't speaking, you may receive a lot of unsolicited opinions about why that is. Parents are often assured that all kids develop at their own pace, and it seems even experts can't agree on what is normal. Some pediatricians refer a child to early intervention at fifteen months and others wait until the child is past two years of age.

When parents ask me if they should take their child in for an evaluation, my answer is almost always yes. Early-intervention services are federally mandated, cover children ages birth to three years, include an evaluation by a professional, and are usually free to parents. If you are unsure where to start, you can talk to your pediatrician and ask for a referral or call your local school district and ask for the number to early intervention or Child Find services. The evaluation must include cognitive, speech-language, physical, social-emotional, and adaptive-developmental areas. The evaluation will determine if your child qualifies for services. It's always better to test and know what you're dealing with than to wait and potentially delay important therapy.

Once it is determined that a child qualifies for speech services, know that children who have CAS may or may not respond to the traditional methods of teaching, such as language stimulation, which is common in many early-intervention programs. However, their response is not likely to produce the gains in speech production that would be expected unless a motor-based approach to therapy is employed. Parents and professionals should be aware of the early signs and symptoms of CAS, and if CAS is suspected, treatment should be changed and provided under a provisional label, such as suspected CAS. Many times, it may be a parent who is the one to suspect apraxia, and if that is the case, it may be worth it to find a local expert who can provide a differential diagnosis or at least an expert consultation. The Apraxia Kids website is an excellent resource that has a "Find a Professional" tab to help parents find local experts in their area.

Early signs and possible symptoms of apraxia in children under three may include difficulty with nursing and/or feeding, lack of babbling or limited babbling, words heard once or twice and then not again, a go-to word or sound used to represent many different things, other delayed motor skills, and/or difficulty imitating non-speech motor tasks, such as puckering or smiling.

Behavioral markers that may be seen in a motor speech exam used to diagnose apraxia include inconsistent errors, difficulty in smooth articulatory transitions between sounds and syllables, errors with prosody particularly with syllabic or phrasal stress, use of simple syllable shapes, limited consonant and vowel repertoire, syllable segregation referring to pauses in between sounds, syllables or words, vowel errors, and/or the presence of oral apraxia (sometimes referred to as "oral motor apraxia"). Oral apraxia is a term to describe difficulties with non-speech, oral-motor tasks, such as going from a pucker to a smile, blowing, rounding the lips, moving the tongue, etc.

Based on our current level of knowledge, diagnosis of CAS before age three can be challenging. Children that are nonverbal and cannot imitate or attempt to imitate speech sounds and words should not receive a diagnosis of CAS. In addition, if children's behavior prevents them from partaking in a motor speech exam, they should not receive a diagnosis of CAS either. However, in either scenario, if apraxia is strongly suspected, children can and should be treated under a provisional label and a treatment approach for apraxia should be implemented.

There are many programs that purport to be geared toward the treatment of apraxia. However, the most appropriate are those that incorporate the principles of motor learning. Many speech-language pathologists will need postgraduate training or resources in order to treat apraxia effectively.

For example, in my practice, I am trained in various methods and I am recognized by Apraxia Kids for Advanced Training and Clinical Expertise in childhood apraxia of speech. I have also attended the PROMPT (Prompts for restructuring oral muscular phonetic targets) Level 1 training, the Kaufman Speech to Language Protocol training, and a DTTC (Dynamic Temporal and Tactile Cueing) training. I attend the yearly Apraxia Kids conference regularly to stay abreast of the current research. For the most up-to-date, credible information, visit my website, SLPMommyofApraxia.com; Apraxia-Kids.org; and ASHA.org for expert articles and resources related to treating apraxia.

Through this journey, I have experienced what it is like to parent a child with this diagnosis, as well as how to treat this complex neurological speech disorder as a speech language pathologist. My hope in writing this book is to give perspective, provide education, and create understanding of apraxia for both parents and professionals.

Finally, I hope this book gives a message of hope. My daughter has inspired and continues to inspire me. I once cried, wondering why this had to happen to her. Now I hear her speak and sing, and I no longer wonder. Instead, I am grateful for what the journey has taught us and continues to teach us. I am so grateful for my daughter, apraxia and all. She is the embodiment of inspiration, perseverance, and resilience. My daughter has taught me that the only disability in life is a bad attitude, and that regardless of any challenge, we should wake up each day with a smile and be happy to be alive.

CHAPTER 1

Her Arrival

One day a spirit appeared,
taking up residence in my vessel.
For a time,
two hearts beat together in
a harmony of song.
The sweetest, simplest of songs,
raw,
pure,
visceral.
Your earthly life hinging on mine,
we spoke in tongues only we could understand.
Reminiscent now in your eyes,
windows to our souls.
Love begun before birth
never dies.

It was a Sunday night. I was pacing around the
living room and trying to watch the football game
to take my mind off the contractions, which were

getting more and more uncomfortable and painful. When the game ended, I called my obstetrician and she told me to come to the hospital.

I arrived around 11:00 p.m. with my husband and mother. At around 1:00 a.m., I was given Pitocin to induce labor since I was having contractions but not dilating or effacing. At one point the obstetrician suggested we do a C-section, but I dismissed it. As the contractions became stronger, I was given an epidural, and vaginal fetal electrodes were placed on the baby's head to monitor activity. They gave me an oxygen mask that I kept discarding because I wasn't struggling to breathe and didn't understand the need for it. During my contractions, the staff seemed very concerned about what they saw on the monitors. The obstetrician came in a second time and recommended a C-section, which I again declined. The pain meds made it difficult to think straight, and not realizing anything was wrong, I still wanted to try and to deliver her naturally.

The night wore on with very little progression. The lights were dimmed as we all tried to get some sleep. As the monitors beeped slowly and rhythmically, I looked over at my mom and husband trying to rest, and I felt so loved.

That blissful feeling abated as quickly as it had

come. My obstetrician returned and became upset that I had my oxygen mask off. As she and the nurses bustled around the computers and monitors, she started to lecture, "Laura you have got to keep this mask on for the baby."

I immediately snapped out of my haze. "This oxygen is for the baby?" I cried incredulously.

My mom furrowed her brow. She looked at me and said, "Laura, you need to do the C-section."

My mind started racing. This wasn't how I had planned my birth story. I was scared, but I knew the baby was in harm's way and what I had to do.

I signed the consent and I was rushed to the operating room. It was incredibly cold. The room was full of doctors and nurses in scrubs with masks over their faces. A bright light was shining down on me, and a big, blue curtain hid our view. It felt so impersonal. I didn't want to deliver my baby this way. My anxiety was in overdrive.

Finally, the big moment arrived. My baby girl was lifted in the air and I was immediately overcome with emotion. My precious Ashlynn was finally here! I cried tears of joy listening to her first cries.

My husband cut the umbilical cord and they cleaned and wrapped her before placing her in my arms. I fell absolutely and completely in love with her.

As I snuggled my perfect baby, I thought about how I couldn't wait to show her this world and teach her everything I could. As an SLP, I had visions and dreams of her being this incredibly verbose child with a large vocabulary. But I had no way of knowing then all the challenges we would face together—and work to overcome—in the next several years.

CHAPTER 2

Milestones and Delays

They told me you were my baby girl,
as you cried hello to us.
I believed them at the time,
Amid the chaos and the fuss.

They told me you were my baby girl,
and when I took you home,
I would gaze upon the sweetest face
I had ever yet to know.

They told me you were my baby girl,
and I would gaze at you at night.
I would watch your sleeping lips
flash smiles radiant and bright.

They told me you were my baby girl,
but I have so many flaws,
and you are perfect in every way.
They must have got it wrong.

They told me you were my baby girl,
and my baby girl you will always be.
But I know the truth and the truth is,
God sent an angel to me.

Ashlynn was a sweet and quiet baby. She started sleeping for six hours a night at four weeks old and had a very happy demeanor. I was a typical first-time mother, anxiously tracking her developmental milestones and eager to see her grow and change. Everything she did brought me joy. Every new movement and new expression would bring happiness to my heart. During this early time in her life, as is common with children with apraxia, she met most of the milestones on time, however that would soon change.

Many newborns have difficulty with breastfeeding and Ashlynn struggled to latch when nursing. This was not unusual, but, looking back, I can see this was the first sign of potential difficulty coordinating and using her oral muscles. However, I worked with a lactation consultant and learned how to have her latch properly. I went on to breastfeed her for close to a year. I was proud that not only had I birthed life; I could sustain it through my body alone.

In her first few months, Ashlynn was able to track with her eyes, smile, giggle, and even roll over.

However, I began to suspect something was wrong when she was about six months of age. Though I spoke to her constantly, she didn't babble at all. She smiled, cooed, and laughed, but made no sounds resembling words. Friends and family members told me I was being too picky because I was an expert, an SLP, but in my heart, I knew something wasn't right.

Typically, babies should start babbling a string of sounds between four and six months of age. This is called "reduplicated babbling" and refers to the stage in which a baby repeats a sound combination, such as "mamamama" or "babababa." Between seven months to a year, babies begin "variegated babbling," including more sounds, which might sound like "buhmuhduhmuhbuh." A lack of babbling or limited babbling within the first year of life can be an early red flag for CAS or other speech/language issues.

At every regular doctor checkup, I filled out developmental questionnaires and realized that Ashlynn was continuing to fall behind in many areas. At six months, she couldn't sit alone without help and she couldn't even get up on her legs and rock back and forth. She would coo (making sounds such as "ahh" and "ohhh"), but she still could not babble (adding consonant sounds to the cooing). I'm thankful her pediatrician had me fill out these screenings so that we were able to start addressing her issues, but I dreaded doing them every time. It's not easy to see that your child is falling behind.

Despite my almost constant visual modeling and babbling to her, Ashlynn would only smile and giggle. I didn't understand. I put her in front of mirrors so she could see her mouth, but she seemed disinterested. I consulted with other colleagues who mostly told me not to worry and to continue with what I was doing. One colleague who worked in early intervention (EI) told me that lack of babbling might be a sign of CAS. She then asked me more questions before assuring me it sounded more like delayed speech and suggested I try baby signing. I wanted so much to believe she would catch up and be fine that I put apraxia out of my mind, though I did began signing with her. I had a book from an old mentor of mine by Joy Collins, called *Baby Signs*, and bought the popular *Signing Time* series by Rachel Coleman. Unfortunately, she couldn't imitate my signs. What I didn't realize at the time was that this was also a possible indicator of more global motor-planning issues.

By the time Ashlynn was 18 months, I could no longer pretend her development was just delayed. At this age, kids go through a "language explosion," adding new words to their vocabulary almost daily.

Each month I waited for this milestone and each month passed without her meeting it. My mother-in-law assured me that my husband didn't talk until the age of three, when he suddenly started speaking in full sentences. I kept holding onto hope that this was the case with her. Dr. Camarata, in his book *Late-Talking Children*, argues that for some children, late talking is just a stage with no other long-term complications.

Though it's true that some children start talking later with no issues, not every child who talks late will catch up without some sort of intervention. Like me, many parents want to believe their child's speech is just delayed and may not seek early intervention through Child Find. However, I strongly recommend doing so, since there is no downside to an evaluation. At worst, you will have spent a few hours to discover that nothing is wrong with your child, and if there is a developmental issue, you will have the opportunity for your child to begin any necessary therapies. Every state has a "birth to age three" early-intervention program that is authorized on Part C of the Individuals with Disabilities Education Act (IDEA). This service is usually free and assesses all pertinent developmental domains of a child. You can reach Child Find through your local school district or ask for a referral from your pediatrician.

When Ashlynn was around two years old, my colleagues encouraged me to take her in for an evaluation. I don't know if it was pride or denial, but I just couldn't bring myself to do it, worrying what they would think of me. As an SLP, I thought I must be terrible at my job if my own child couldn't talk, despite knowing that a speech delay or disorder often has no known cause. Children learn to talk even in homes where there is very little language. I tell heartsick parents daily that it is not their fault. However, I still felt I had failed her. What's the point in having a mom who is a speech therapist if she can't even teach you to talk?

Every day after work I would come home exhausted, and yet I would somehow summon the energy to work with my daughter. I was using an approach called "language stimulation," a common technique employed by most early intervention SLPs. Focused language stimulation involves choosing a speech or language target and introducing activities to encourage the child's attempt at said target. For example, a clinician might wish to encourage early developing sounds of /p/, /b/, and /m/. They might come with a bagful of toys designed to elicit these speech targets such as a bottle of bubbles and model words such as "bubble," "pop," "up," and "more." Though strategically targeted, relatively few demands are placed on the child and the child is never instructed to say something specific. Rather, language stimulation techniques employ fun toys and relatively simply speech or language targets and rely on fun and engaging interactions between the child and the SLP. These activities are done in the child's natural environment, which promotes carryover into spontaneous speech. The idea is that through this targeted exposure, the child will begin to make speech and language gains.

During this time, Ashlynn did make some gains. Before spring break, when she was two and a half, she had only about five to ten core words—labeling things like "Mama," "Dada," and "doggie." By the end of spring break, after working with her full-time, she was able to request juice, water, and milk with one prompt (where I asked her to tell me what she wanted before giving her the item). Her grandmothers immediately noticed and told me how great it was she was talking more. I was so pleased to hear their feedback, but at the same time, I felt guilty for working. Here I was helping other children when my own child was at home *needing* me.

By summer, when Ashlynn was a few months shy of her third birthday, she had added quite a few more words and had reached around fifty expressive words. Again, everyone noticed and celebrated her success, but I could only focus on the fact that this milestone is usually achieved for children around two years of age, which meant she was about eight months behind. When summer came, we did therapy all day. At breakfast she had to choose between two items and attempt to ask for one of them while pointing. The same went for play activities. We sang our ABCs and nursery rhymes all morning, and on our walks, we played "I spy" ("I see," in our case, because Ashlynn couldn't yet say "spy"). We did activities that focused on final consonants in words. For example, I had a wagon with a variety of rocks and sticks to practice final *K*. I had speech CDs, such as *Animation Station*, that I played every time we were in the car and then reinforced during our play activities. We paired gross motor activities like moving a car or pushing the swing and saying "go." We tried everything.

Despite all this effort, Ashlynn still couldn't sing the alphabet, and she couldn't put two words together without my prompting her word by word. On social media, I saw a friend's daughter—younger than Ashlynn—singing the alphabet beautifully and another friend's daughter singing "You Are My Sunshine" with 95 percent intelligibility at age two and a half. My nephew, who just turned two talked to us on FaceTime and was able to put two words together such as "dog little" and "baby sleep." I'll admit, it was hard to be happy for them.

Instead, I felt sad and embarrassed because I believed Ashlynn's speech was a reflection on myself as her mother and her SLP.

The pediatrician offered a referral to early intervention for a speech delay, but I still wasn't ready. I was convinced that another SLP couldn't do any more in one session a week than what I was doing with Ashlynn every day. We continued with baby signing, even though she only caught on to a few signs, and we played while making various sounds. I bought a play zoo and farm and made the noises the various animals make while she sat quietly and giggled. I would ask Ashlynn to say "moo" or "quack," and she would just smile. We played with cars and pull toys while I made the sounds "vroom," "bonk," and "beep beep." She wouldn't utter a sound. I read repetitive books such as *Brown Bear, Brown Bear, What Do You See?*, and books that had animal or vehicle sounds, such as *Mr. Brown Can Moo! Can You?*. Still nothing.

I was so frustrated as the days went on, but I continued to work with her every night after work *knowing* that these researched techniques should work eventually. I remembered reading a study regarding the Hanen approach of teaching parents how to work with their children with a speech delay. In it, the authors said that techniques used by parents

of typically developing children are often aban-
doned by parents of children with a speech delay
because they don't appear to be working. If there is
no reward or positive feedback for the parent (for
example, the child mooing when the parent moos),
then the parent is likely to stop. I was determined
not to be that parent; I was going to stick with the
techniques.

My son, Jace, was born in July 2012. After so long
working with Ashlynn every night, now I had almost no time to devote to her. It was a difficult ad-
justment for both of us. She was so used to getting
one-on-one time with me every day, and now she
had none. I felt guilty; I was sleep deprived and exhausted. I finally decided to take her to Child Find
for an evaluation. When I made that appointment,
I felt like I had failed her. What I realized later is
that I had actually saved her.

CHAPTER 3

Evaluation and IEP

Sleep now, baby girl,
I'll help you fall asleep.
Don't fight your heavy lids,
that are begging for some peace.

Sleep now, baby girl,
I'll hold you in my arms.
Rest comfortably on my chest,
as I keep you safe from harm.

Sleep now, baby girl,
the sun will come so soon.
I hope you have pleasant dreams,
beneath the light of the moon.

Sleep now, baby girl,
oh, you're growing way too fast.
I try to enjoy each moment,
because I know they won't last.

Sleep now, baby girl,
I hold you to me close.
My heart smiles with your cuddles,
and sings to you in prose.

Sleep now, baby girl,
in arms that love you so,
and I will forever cherish these moments,
as you continue to grow.

It was the day of Ashlynn's evaluation with Child Find at a school near my house. I wanted to turn around and go home at least three different times, but I didn't. We pulled into the parking lot of the school, and I held her tiny hand as we headed straight toward the big, blue doors. I hit the button attached to the speaker and stared at it as I waited to be let in.

We were shuffled into a room where they checked Ashlynn's hearing and vision, and then moved to another room full of toys and equipment where they performed a transdisciplinary play-based assessment, commonly used by special education teams when evaluating children under the age of three. Professionals on transdisciplinary teams share roles across disciplinary boundaries with each professional looking at the child's complete profile of communication, social, cognitive, and physical strengths and weaknesses. It was odd to be on the other end, looking from the outside in. I realized how intimidating it feels. They were judging my baby, my heart. It felt awful and scary.

I wondered what they were thinking. I wanted to scoop Ashlynn up and leave, but I also knew this was the first step on her journey of learning to speak.

Luckily, I didn't have to wait long. After her evaluation, the SLP came to talk to me and she said four words that I will never forget. "Laura, this is apraxia." I instantly realized she was right. At two years and eleven months, I finally learned Ashlynn couldn't speak because she had apraxia.

My God. How did I miss that? I knew she had at best a speech delay or at worst a speech disorder, but apraxia? It was apraxia.

Apraxia.

Apraxia.

It started to sink in. Oh God no, not apraxia. My mind flashed to the kids I had seen in my therapy practice who had entered kindergarten and still weren't talking. Oh no. No. Why *my* baby? I felt sick. My head started spinning. The rest of the evaluation was a blur. I could tell Ashlynn was also delayed in all her motor milestones, but I couldn't stop thinking about the apraxia diagnosis. I walked out with my head in a fog. I was given papers about what to do with her at home to help spur language development. I stared incredulously at them. Did this woman think I, an SLP, wasn't already doing all of this with Ashlynn? I felt so incredibly inadequate.

These papers were very familiar to me. They were suggestions based on language-focused stimulation and I had been using these strategies now for months. They weren't working. Ironically, none of the papers were tailored to helping children with apraxia. They were just a standard set of handouts given to every parent who had a child that qualified for speech/language services.

Apraxia.

That's why those techniques weren't working. My mind was reeling.

As I put Ashlynn in her car seat, half in a daze, I heard her sweet voice say her favorite word as she looked up at me, searching my face.

"Hi?" she ventured.

I was preoccupied and didn't answer.

"Hi?" she pressed with more inflection than before.

As my eyes met hers, I saw Ashlynn was staring at me. I realized I had tears in my eyes and my head was full of worry. Her sweet face looking up at me made me cry harder. No. No. Not apraxia. I hugged her while she was sitting in her car seat and my chest started heaving and I felt like I couldn't breathe. I sent a text to an SLP friend, "She has apraxia. I'm devastated."

My sweet baby. My perfect, perfect baby. The angel God had sent to me had one of the most severe speech disorders in children. I was so confused. How did I, an SLP, end up with a child with apraxia?

My mother-in-law had been watching my baby. "So? How'd it go?" she asked innocently when we got home.

I broke down again and started crying. "She has apraxia!" I wailed.

Instantly, tears appeared in her face as she questioned, "Will she ever talk?"

"Oh, yes," I responded. "She just has to climb the biggest hills in order to do it."

I cried some more.

I'm not sure what's worse: being a parent who doesn't know what apraxia really is or being a parent who knows *exactly* what the monster is and just how much work will be required to overcome it.

I know I sound dramatic when I say I was distraught. After all, there are children who get diagnosed with fatal disorders. My daughter would just have trouble speaking. Regardless, rational or not, I felt utterly and absolutely devastated. A mentor had once told me to remember that every child is their parents' perfect baby, and now I truly understood. If you are a professional reading this, I beg you to consider what the parents are feeling. Hearing my child had a speech disorder was **awful.** I knew my child was delayed. I *knew* yet hearing another professional confirm my worst fears felt terrible.

The next step, after the evaluations qualified Ashlynn for services, was to have the Individualized Education Program (IEP) meeting at school. An IEP is a legal document that outlines the educational plan for a child with disabilities, including the child's specific goals and specific services that will be provided in order to meet those goals. The meeting was not what I expected, which was unexpected, since I regularly attended IEP meetings as a school SLP.

Despite knowing Ashlynn had apraxia, the school professionals kept stressing a "language-rich environment," which is great for all children but won't fix the problem of apraxia, as it does not focus on the underlying speech motor planning problem. They also told me all services would be in the classroom, even though based on our current understanding of motor learning and a growing body of research, the suggestion is usually intense, direct, one-on-one therapy. After hearing their therapy plan, I suspected that the school SLP knew little about apraxia and how to treat it.

Being in the profession, I am well versed as to my rights as a parent to a child with a disability, but unfortunately, not all parents have this background. Most parents at the initial evaluation have no idea what to expect, and even parents who have attended numerous IEP meetings may be unaware of their rights or not understand the terminology. These rights should be provided to parents at every meeting per the Individuals with Disabilities Education Act (IDEA), a federal law, however this document will not necessarily answer all a parent's questions.

I highly recommend parents learn about their child's rights in special education through reading books on the topic or using online resources such as Wright's Law. Additionally, an advocate is often crucial, someone who knows the law and the IEP process, who can help parents make informed decisions, and who can attend IEP meeting(s) with parents. IDEA requires there be an agency in each state where parents can find help. Wright's Law online provides a directory of state Parent Training and Information Centers (PTI) and Community Parent Resource Centers (CPRC).

CHAPTER 4

Life Before Ashlynn

One summer day, I dreamed a dream,
a dream I dreamed with you.
One spring day I saw the dream,
I dreamed come true with you.

One spring night, I dreamed a life,
a life I dreamed with you.
One summer day I lived the dream,
I dreamed come true with you.

One winter night, I dreamed a family,
a family I'd have with you.
On one fall night she was born to us,
a dream to make all others come true.

One fall night, you dreamed a dream,
a dream you shared with me,
and very soon your dream will
become reality.

CAS was not unknown to me. It had been a topic of intense interest to me ever since I was a speech-language pathology assistant (SLPA). Apraxia is often misunderstood, even among the SLP and professional communities. This is due, in part, to the fact it was only recognized as a separate and distinct speech disorder in 2007 by the American Speech-Language-Hearing Association (ASHA), the certifying entity and professional body for speech-language pathologists in the United States. Many SLPs have heard about CAS but may not have the skills or experience to correctly diagnose and/or treat it. Because it is considered a rare speech disorder, few SLPs have seen many children with it through which they could develop expertise.

My first encounter with apraxia came when I was an SLPA at my first school position. I was working under another mentor, Deborah Comfort, who had requested an SLPA (me) to assist her with a student who was nonverbal with apraxia. She took me to a professional development workshop given by Ruth Stoeckel from the Mayo Clinic. Dr. Stoeckel worked with Edythe Strand, who developed Dynamic Temporal and Tactile Cueing, a motor-based treatment approach for apraxia that was adapted from the integral stimulation method that was initially used to treat adults with apraxia. According to Strand and Debertine, "Dynamic

Temporal and Tactile Cueing (DTTC) is a method that uses a cueing hierarchy (auditory, visual, and tactile) and systematically decreases supports as the child achieves success at each level of the cueing hierarchy." There are free YouTube videos from Dr. Edythe Strand outlining the method, along with a website, childapraxiatreatment.org, that has numerous resources and includes a link to a free training through the University of Texas at Dallas.

Fresh from the training, my mentor developed a treatment plan based on Dr. Stoeckel's presentation and the DTTC method. She saw this boy two days a week, and I saw the child a third day. Children with apraxia, especially in the early stages, need intense and frequent individual speech therapy. I didn't have much experience, but I could tell CAS was *very* different from other speech disorders—not only in presentation, but also in how it is treated. I'm so thankful for this pivotal first experience that set me on the right course for best practice in apraxia therapy.

Two years later, I became the SLP in an elementary school within the same district. I was excited and nervous to be the building's only expert in childhood speech-language disorders. My school was considered a Title 1 school, which has a high number of children living in poverty. These kids generally only receive state-funded services and don't have access to private services since many insurance companies don't cover speech therapy. I felt so much pressure knowing that, in many cases, I might be the only person some children would see to help them improve their speech and language skills.

My first challenging student was a new kindergartener named David. He won my heart immediately. He had a million-dollar smile and was sweet, friendly, playful, and funny. Unfortunately, his classmates couldn't see what I saw because David couldn't talk and, in frustration, would often hit the other kids. His IEP stated that he had a basic speech delay, but we weren't making any progress in speech or language. Early in the school year when I was working with him, David saw an alphabet bingo game on my shelf and took it down. He proceeded to name most of the letters. This child who had not said *one* word to anyone was somehow able to do this. I was blown away. However, when I tried to have him sequence those sounds with another sound, he couldn't. I immediately suspected apraxia and I changed his service delivery to four days a week and we began intense therapy sessions.

Though I had been to graduate school, I was taught very little about treating CAS. It was not formally mentioned in my textbooks and I was given maybe a dozen loose pages about it. The consensus in my graduate school program was that it was very rare, and we would likely never see it. This is important for parents to know. There are still professors today who tell their preprofessional students that CAS is a myth and just a more severe presentation of phonological disorder. Today there are some graduate programs that are including CAS in the coursework, but from my experience and talking to other SLPs, I believe this is still the exception and not the norm. Unless SLPs have sought out additional training in apraxia, it is very unlikely they have the background knowledge and skills to effectively treat it.

Fortunately, I recalled my days as an SLPA and the informational materials I had from going to the workshop I had attended by Dr. Stoeckel. I found the Apraxia Kids website, which was full of articles from national apraxia experts that I printed out and referenced. Far from qualified, I, at least, was armed with these resources.

David was the hardest worker. He was so motivated, and despite repetitive and intense drills, he tackled them all and never once complained. By the end of that semester, his dad heard him say, "Hi, Dad," for the first time. So overcome with joy, his father cried. David's smile had never been bigger. We had practiced so long and so hard just to get those two words out and he had done it! That was my first personal experience with how heartbreaking it is to have a child who can't talk, but also, how amazing it feels when they finally do.

I can't help but wonder what would have happened to David had I not had that early experience with apraxia in my time as an SLPA. What if I had not found the Apraxia Kids website and downloaded all the information I could? Would David still be preverbal? After all, he had been in speech therapy since early intervention. How many SLPs had he experienced before me? Why had it taken until two months into kindergarten for anyone to realize he had apraxia?

This is the heartbreaking reality of apraxia. There are very few graduate programs that adequately detail apraxia, so unless a clinician has had prior experience in their clinicals or they have received postgraduate training in apraxia, it is unlikely they are skilled or qualified to treat it. I say this only to encourage SLPs to take postgraduate training courses in apraxia if you have a child with apraxia on your caseload.

Despite this, I'm encouraged for the future thanks to the efforts of the Apraxia Kids organization. Many are surprised to learn that apraxia has only been officially recognized as a separate and unique disorder by ASHA since 2007. Apraxia Kids has been hosting yearly national conferences on apraxia since 2005, and more research is coming out every year related to apraxia. In addition, there are now walks for apraxia that raise awareness, and the United States Congress proclaimed May 14 "Apraxia Awareness Day" in 2013.

CHAPTER 5

The Journey Begins

You went to speak, but the words wouldn't come,
stuck in your brain, so easy for some.

You went to crawl with the best of intents,
yet your body didn't know what your brain meant.

You went to walk, big smiles and all,
yet every time you tried, it ended with a fall.

You went to drink from a big girl cup,
you would sputter and spit till it came up.

A new car for Christmas, kids want to ride,
spins in circles, hard to learn how to drive.

But,

you are a living example to persevere,
and with it you conquer all our fears.

One day you said, "Mommy," and "I love you."
One day you crawled to Daddy's shoe.

You don't just walk, but now you run.
You drink from any cup till it's done.

And I know in time, you will do it all.
With more patience and practice,
you will conquer it all.

After Ashlynn's apraxia diagnosis sunk in, I picked myself up and brushed myself off. I had no choice. It was time to dig in and get to work. We started with getting her an IEP and therapy at school, but I also explored other options.

Before I had a child with a speech delay/disorder, I could never have imagined how important time is to a parent. You don't want your child to spend one more minute trapped inside a mouth that isn't working. Seeing my daughter hit or tantrum out of frustration was heartbreaking. Every second, every minute, every hour, and every day that passed with her unable to speak were moments we would never get back.

I decided I needed to put her into private therapy.

I would have to use my savings that I was holding for my maternity leave, but I decided Ashlynn couldn't wait. There was so much research showing that early intervention was key, and as her mom *and* as an SLP, I knew she was at a prime stage in development to effect the most change. Ashlynn was open and willing to practice. We had to act now.

As much as I prided myself on keeping up on the current research, at the time I was not an expert on apraxia. The scope of practice for speech-language pathology is extremely vast and it grows every day. An SLP is responsible for articulation and phonology disorders, receptive and/or expressive language disorder, stuttering, cluttering, speech-language delay, hearing loss/disability, auditory processing disorder, autism, voice disorders and pathology, traumatic brain injury, aphasia, dysphagia, dysarthria, apraxia, and cleft lip and palate. In addition, SLPs are technically certified to work with both adult and child populations, and have knowledge of various syndromes, disorders, and diseases, and their effect on speech, language, and communication. For example, just in my practice alone, I have seen that apraxia can coincide with a variety of other disorders such as cerebral palsy, Down syndrome, Fragile X syndrome, or agenesis of the corpus collosum. Although my treatment approach is still rooted in principles of motor learning, understanding the additional individual profile of each person and their comorbidities (a term used to describe any additional diagnoses) is essential when treating each child.

Most often, SLPs are a bit like a general practitioner. They have knowledge and training in most speech, language, and communication disorders, but they are typically only specialists in treating the most common issues. School-based SLPs are usually experts in phonological, articulation, and language disorders. They are also the best at understanding and knowing how speech and language disorders affect a child's social and academic performance in the classroom. They provide critical insight as to how the child's speech or language disorder affects them during their academic life. However, the average school-based SLP will not see as many less-prevalent disorders, such as apraxia or stuttering. Although technically qualified to treat these disorders, they may or may not have expertise. This is where private therapy comes in.

After that first IEP meeting, I decided I wanted to get expert help for Ashlynn from someone who dealt with apraxia daily or almost daily. I took her to a private SLP who came recommended by other mothers of children with apraxia. I left the session with my mommy sense saying, "Yes. This is exactly what we needed." The SLP was extremely knowledgeable in treating apraxia, knew and seemed to quote many of the references in the literature, and had Ashlynn working to talk the entire time. I was so excited not only for Ashlynn, but also for me to learn from her as I set out to become an expert in this disorder as well.

Many parents, when faced with an apraxia diagnosis, don't even know where to begin. They may or may not be aware there are specific treatment approaches for apraxia that are different from traditional approaches. They might not know what questions to ask or they might assume all SLPs are equally skilled in treating apraxia.

Fortunately, we have the nonprofit organization Apraxia Kids. It has a website packed with information and even has a search function where a parent can find an SLP in their area who has received postgraduate training in CAS. Parents should not be afraid to ask questions. Call therapy offices and press them for the answers you need.

I admit it was incredibly difficult to take my daughter to another SLP. I had so much guilt and shame. I remember feeling so embarrassed that I didn't know how to help her. The only thing that kept me walking into that office week after week was that my desire to help my daughter was stronger than my pride. In my practice, I have now come to learn moms, in general, feel judged by everyone, but especially moms who have kids with unique needs. We feel judged by family, friends, teachers, and therapists. The best anyone in the family's life can do is recognize that the family is doing the best they can.

I remember during this time having two big wishes. One I wanted to know that there was an adult who had grown up with apraxia and was now living a successful life. Two, I wanted to find another SLP who had a child with apraxia, someone who could understand what I was going through. The parent support group I was in on Facebook was helpful, but only another SLP who has a child with apraxia could understand how it felt to work in speech therapy yet be unable to help your child talk.

The SLP treating Ashlynn used an approach called the Kaufman Speech to Language Protocol (K-SLP). It was developed by Nancy Kaufman, CCC-SLP, who specializes in providing treatment to kids with CAS. It was an entirely different way of doing therapy than anything else I had seen to that point or been taught. According to her website, "The K-SLP focuses upon the child's motor-speech skills, shaping the consonants, vowels and syllable shapes/gestures from what they are capable of producing toward higher levels of motor-speech coordination, giving them a functional avenue by which to become an effective vocal communicator."

It included a very direct form of teaching word approximations, paired with visual cues. Therapy started at the smallest syllable level, teaching her to say words like "two" and "day," and progressed to having her combine the syllables to produce the word "today." Each sound and syllable increment were shaped to a closer version of the adult form and then expanded.

Ashlynn loved practicing the Kaufman cards. She would work on them in therapy and at home and show us all the words she could say on the cards. She would beam with pride as she recited them. I was thrilled and finally felt like we were on the right track.

I used to watch Ashlynn in therapy as I held my baby son. She sat in a chair and dutifully repeated and said words on the card deck, day after day. I remember thinking that I had a Kaufman card deck in the school I worked at, but I really didn't know or understand the theory behind it until I saw it in action. I marveled at how I was never taught this in any of my schooling, practicums, clinicals, or internships. I was never even taught that apraxia *required* a completely different treatment approach than other speech sound disorders.

Since I've gone on to specialize in CAS, I now know that the current research available suggests therapy for apraxia needs to be based on the principles of motor learning, since apraxia is a problem with the planning and programming of the motor movements needed for speech. Today there are more therapy approaches for CAS that have been shown to have success in the research with the strongest level of evidence for DTTC (Dynamic Temporal Tactile Cueing) and related integral stimulation-based approaches, and ReST (Rapid Syllable Transition Treatment). Though varying somewhat, like the K-SLP approach that my daughter had, they all share principles of motor learning.

Maas, et al (2008), provides a tutorial in a research paper he wrote on the principles of motor learning and its application to motor speech disorders such as apraxia. These principles include items like target selection, the structure of practice, and different practice schedules, and the types of feedback provided in the treatment program. Essentially, parents should see a lot of repetition of speech targets in therapy sessions. Speech targets may be difficult but attainable, with cues and help from the SLP. Finally, parents may notice that the type of feedback the SLP provides to the child changes over time, moving from specific feedback (for example, "Start with your lips out") to more general feedback ("That's right") as the child gains success.

It's very important that I point out **there is not one best approach for childhood apraxia of speech.** Many times, parents will hear a presentation, go to a conference, or read a book on one approach and then become convinced that it is the only approach that will help their child. This may not be true. The best approach is to find an SLP who is skilled with apraxia therapy and who uses the principles of motor learning. It's also important that the child and the therapist are a good fit. If a child is regularly crying before or within therapy, this is a red flag. The child's therapist should be informed, and parents should see changes in therapy to address the issue. In some instances, parents might want to consider switching therapists.

There are several resources for finding an SLP who specializes in CAS:

- Apraxia-Kids.org: https://www.apraxia-kids.org/speech-pathologist-directory/

- ASHA.org: https://www.asha.org/profind/

I always encourage parents to ask questions and to not be afraid to question an SLP's methods. If the clinician is skilled and confident in what they are doing, no question will be offensive, and they will be happy to explain the reasoning. Other considerations include the relationship an SLP has with a particular child. Sometimes even the most skilled clinician may not be a match, and it's okay to move on and try another.

CHAPTER 6

Starting Preschool

If I could take away the hardship,

you would never feel success.

If I sheltered you from pain,

you'd be even more different than the rest.

If I kept you in a bubble, safe inside all day,

you wouldn't feel the rain, or the warm sun's rays.

None of that matters though, I can't take it away.

But I promise I'll stand beside you each step of the way.

Before the Apraxia conference and after my IEP experience, I had mixed emotions on Ashlynn's first day of preschool. I was excited and hopeful that she would finally get the additional speech and language intervention she needed, and skeptical because it didn't seem like her teacher or SLP would be the ones able to do so.

I dropped off her private speech report to the teacher and SLP so they could see her progress and what seemed to be currently helping her.

I was pleasantly surprised to see there were four kids and three adults in the room. Talk about a great student/teacher ratio! There was the teacher, the teacher's assistant (TA), and then, depending on the day, either the occupational therapist (OT) or the SLP.

On the first day, I received a weekly lesson plan. It was so helpful, because even though Ashlynn couldn't tell me what she did at school, I could look at the agenda and talk to her about her day. That day, Ashlynn came home, and we ate lunch. While she was eating, she balled up part of her sandwich, hid it in her fist, and asked me playfully, "Wherdido?"

When I repeated, "Where did it go?" she laughed, opened her fist, and said, "Right der!"

Now she had been saying "Right there!" for a month or so, but this "Where'd it go?" was new. She played the game and used the phrase the whole day, obviously proud of herself.

When Ashlynn started preschool, she was talking more at home, but she still wasn't saying much in class. For example, her first word was, "Hi," and she would say it happily and readily to anyone once she was twelve months old. When she entered school at age three, it took her months to say it to anyone. Six months later, a note came home that said she did it without prompting. I was happy she was doing it at school, but it sure didn't feel like progress to me. There would be many examples like this.

"She's counting consistently to five!" they told me at one meeting. I gave them a polite smile. Ashlynn had been counting to twenty for months now.

"Ashlynn knows the letters of her name!" they told me one day. I smiled politely. She had been able to find or point to most of the letters since before preschool.

"She's talking to peers, but still doesn't have a lot of pretend play." I gave a half-smile. Ashlynn had been engaging in pretend play games with her brother every day at home.

However, though Ashlynn wasn't always able to talk to her classmates, she did try to interact with them and with the teacher, which gave me hope that eventually she would make friends. One day I observed her class. At one point, a peer was off to the side, crying, and Ashlynn could not take her eyes off the child. While the other kids danced to music, Ashlynn noticed her friend wasn't participating and moved over to dance beside her. She held her hand out as if to say, "I see you. You matter. I don't want you to be sad."

During the dancing activity, Ashlynn moved from peer to peer. Laughing with them, engaging them with her smile, not her words. It felt amazing to know that Ashlynn, despite her limited language skills, was connecting with her peers.

Ashlynn was bringing home art projects frequently, and one day she brought home a tree and a wreath made with fall leaves. While eating lunch that day, I asked her if she sang the song "Autumn Leaves Are Falling Down," which I had seen in the lesson plan. She kind of said "yeah" and so we sang it. When she was done, she said "see" for sing. I asked her what she wanted me to sing and she said "bee . . . bu bu bee." I didn't understand and so she started trying to sing the melody to the "Baby Bumblebee" song. I asked her if she was singing "Baby Bumblebee" at school and started singing the song. Ashlynn began doing all the cute little gestures that go with the song. I emailed the teacher to ask if they had sung this song, and she responded that they had been singing it all week. I was so excited that Ashlynn had finally told me something that happened in her day.

In my professional practice, parents of nonverbal or preverbal children frequently have hesitations about sending their child to school. Understandably their worries include fears about bullying or being mistreated and not being able to report what has happened during their day. In my daughter's case, starting school at age three provided an amazing vehicle for her confidence and language development, and I'm so glad I started her when I did. However, her new interactions did make her vulnerable to bullying.

I couldn't believe it could happen in preschool, but I watched it myself every morning at line-up before school started. A certain girl from Ashlynn's class was usually early and already in line when we got there. This child was not nice— she rolled her eyes and bossed Ashlynn around. No matter what Ashlynn did, the girl would tell her what or what not to do. Despite the girl's terrible attitude, Ashlynn walked up to her every morning with a cheery "Hi!" The girl always ignored her.

At one class holiday party I noticed Ashlynn had chosen to sit by this particular girl. Fuming inside, I couldn't figure out why Ashlynn would choose to sit next to her bully. I asked her later why she was sitting next to the girl who was always rude to her in line. Ashlynn's response was, "She sad."

I was shocked.

The next morning was much the same. Ashlynn walked up with her cheery "Hi!" and the girl gestured haughtily to Ashlynn and said, "YOU can get behind me. I am first."

Ashlynn just responded with a sweet "Yes?" as she stepped back. It was then that I realized that Ashlynn only has love in her heart. She was the target, not me, and yet she still greeted this girl happily every day. I had a lot to learn from Ashlynn. There is no room for hatred in our hearts. Ashlynn could tell that this girl was unhappy, and so she always had a smile for her.

I always encourage parents to observe their child's classroom and interview the staff and teachers. Get a feel for it and then listen to your gut. If something doesn't feel right, it probably isn't. Kids with developmental delays do not fit in a neat box. Even kids who share a disorder have unique traits and personalities. Families have different philosophies regarding schooling, with some preferring to home-school. I do not judge a parent for any decision they make, as long as it's an informed decision. Another thing that helped my nerves as a parent was the use of a "back and forth" book that the teacher and therapists would write in to inform me about Ashlynn's day. I highly suggest having this sort of communication tool put in the accommodations section of the IEP.

I observed the classroom several weeks after school started. I was excited to see for myself how Ashlynn was doing. I went for a lot of reasons, but mostly to make sure I liked the classroom and that I could feel confident my daughter's needs were being met. I left that observation in tears.

I sat in the back of the classroom. The class had read *We're Going on a Bear Hunt* by Michael Rosen, and afterward they did an obstacle course that involved the kids jumping on a trampoline with a bar and then crawling like a bear around a table. I watched child after child easily tackle the obstacle course. But, when it was Ashlynn's turn, she couldn't do any of it. She needed help to even get up on the trampoline. Then, instead of jumping, she just marched her little legs up and down. A big smile and beautiful energy, but no jumping. She then needed help getting down and almost fell off. As she went to do her bear crawl, she couldn't hold herself up in that position, so the therapist held her core to help Ashlynn get up on her legs. As she hung from the therapist's arms, basically carried around the obstacle course, I felt my chest tighten and tears form in my eyes.

My mind flashed back to Ashlynn's third-birthday gift: a tricycle. My husband and I took her to the toy store, excited and full of hope and expectation. I had seen two-year old children on social media gleefully riding their trikes with big, goofy smiles on their faces, and I couldn't wait to snap that picture of my little girl.

As we left the store, I had visions of me walking to the park, with Ashlynn riding her trike in front. I would occasionally have to call for her to stop so she wouldn't get too far ahead, but it was me getting too far ahead that night. When Ashlynn tried the trike, she couldn't even keep her feet on the pedals straight, much less pedal and steer. As I stared at her that day in class, I realized that not only was she behind in speech, she was way behind in motor skills, compared to the other children. It didn't make sense to me. She was getting physical therapy and occupational therapy, in addition to all the other therapies. It was heartbreaking. I had no explanation for her delay in motor skills except for "global developmental delay," the label identified by the school district.

"She's a puzzle," Ashlynn's school physical therapist told me one day.

"A puzzle?" I thought to myself. A puzzle is something that has many pieces that must be put together to complete. I didn't want to hear that my daughter was a puzzle. A puzzle is something that one might not figure out. It was heartbreaking to know professionals in the field had never seen anything like her. It was discouraging not to have any answers about Ashlynn's delayed motor skills.

I wish I could say that is when the tears stopped, but the heartbreak continued through that first year. It was no secret that my daughter had a short attention span. As a mom I worried, of course, but then, shortly after starting school, her school SLP expressed concern as well.

The SLP asked me to come in to discuss possible strategies for keeping Ashlynn on task in a group setting. She said that taking my daughter out of the classroom had been working great for speech, but the school team didn't want to have to take Ashlynn out of the room for every activity they were doing. I agreed, but my heart sank. I knew Ashlynn had trouble with attention, but much like her speech and now her motor skills, I was hoping that no one else noticed this detail and that I was just being an overly concerned mom. Having it pointed out by someone else made my heart very, very heavy again.

There is this feeling every parent who has a child with some sort of problem can relate to. It is this visceral sensation deep inside you that tells you something is wrong even when you don't want to admit it or even maybe have a name for it. I knew Ashlynn's attention was an issue, but admitting it was too much to bear. On top of the apraxia and the global developmental delay and the heartbreak at watching her hang from that therapist's arms to get the "feel" for a bear crawl, my heart couldn't take anymore.

My poor little girl. I knew that when things were hard for her, she tended to change the subject (or switch her attention to something else since she couldn't really verbalize much yet). However, Ashlynn had a very difficult time attending to anything without getting distracted by something else. What was normal? What was not? I didn't know. I was learning through my online support group that Ashlynn's attention issues were not entirely uncommon in kids with apraxia and could be sensory processing disorder (SPD). Sensory processing disorder has a lot of overlap with attention deficit hyperactivity disorder (ADHD). I knew it was a little too young to diagnose ADHD, but I hoped Ashlynn didn't have that too. She didn't deserve any of this. She was the sweetest, most lovable little girl and she shouldn't have to fight so hard for everything she did or learned.

CHAPTER 7

Language Explosion

Well I came home,
like a stone,
and I fell heavy into your arms.
These days of dust,
which we've known,
will blow away with this new sun.

But I'll kneel down,
wait for now.
And I'll kneel down,
know my ground.

And I will wait, I will wait for you.
And I will wait, I will wait for you.
—Mumford and Sons

As the year progressed and I worried more and more about Ashlynn's motor skills and attention, I was cheering for joy about her speech development. She was progressing by leaps and bounds. Sometimes, I felt like we were actually having a conversation. She could at least tell me where she was hurting, even if she didn't use the right words or language, and she could tell me what she wanted to eat. She started trying to repeat everything and even gained some spontaneous four-word utterances.

One week, I wrote, her new thing was "too," as in, "Ashlynn go ni night, too?" or "Ashlynn eat dinner, too?" That counted as four words! She also said, "I want more ketchup."

After hard work from both her SLPs and myself, Ashlynn started marking every final *T*, *P*, and *N* consonant. Getting to that point, though, wasn't easy. When she was practicing CVC (consonant-vowel-consonant) words, I could see her brain whirling as she groped and/or made a long pause before the final sound. Groping is a characteristic sometimes seen in CAS that is not commonly seen in other speech sound disorders. When children are groping, they may make a mouth posture(s) for a sound or word or appear to be searching for a sound or word but are unable to execute it.

In Ashlynn's case, and in the case of most kids with apraxia, she needed a visual and verbal cue every time. For example, when saying "hat" she would say, "ha-t." The pause time could be up to three seconds, which may not sound like very long but is when you are talking about speech. Disordered pausing contributes to prosodic errors seen in kids with apraxia. Errors with prosody is a diagnostic characteristic that may be present when considering an apraxia diagnosis and can include inappropriate stress, volume, pitch, or rate.

Ashlynn could finally add the final sounds on words without any groping or excessive pause time. Such a small step, but so big at the same time! Having a child with apraxia makes one wonder how we ever learn to talk at all—so much is involved.

Ashlynn experienced a "language explosion" about four to five months into the appropriate apraxia-specific therapy, at age three and a half. Though this typically happens much earlier in a child's development, I was so thrilled my daughter was talking. She put lip balm on her "yip" and had her brother sit in her "yap." She put a "hat" on her head and drank with a "sup." She could tell me perfectly, "I want down," and that she wanted "out" or to put something "in."

She also was tickled by everything and laughed "Silly _____." My favorite was, of course, "Silly Momma," but "Silly baby" and" Silly Daddy" were also popular.

I read Ashlynn books using "cloze procedures," a process where you read a repetitive nursery rhyme or sing a song and insert a pause where a word would be. One of Ashlynn's favorite books was *Five Little Monkeys Jumping on the Bed.* I started pausing before "bed" every time I read it, and then gradually expanded to stopping at "Mama called the doctor and the doctor said, _____." At this point, Ashlynn was just starting to put three to four words together, but she could complete the entire phrase to this book ("No more monkeys jumping on the bed!") if I employed this technique.

Another triumph during this language explosion occurred in the car one day. Mumford and Son's "I Will Wait" was on the radio. I was singing to it, and suddenly, I heard her. Her little voice filled the car with the chorus. There are no words to describe the feeling. As I listened, *really* listened to the lyrics, my eyes welled with tears. I knew that I would always be there for her, that I would always "wait" for her by her side, encouraging her and cheering her on.

These little triumphs are so very sweet when you have a child with a developmental delay. Ashlynn has taught me so much about life, especially to appreciate all the little things so much more. We never took her talking or her singing for granted, not even for a second.

Of course, things weren't always rosy. During this time of language explosion, we went to the park one day. The park had always been bittersweet for me. On the sweet side, Ashlynn loved it and had fun there. On the bitter side, her motor skills were so delayed, she constantly fell or was at risk for falling, and she couldn't talk to the other kids.

One day at the park, however, Ashlynn was talking appropriately to a little girl, saying "Come on!" and "Let's go again!" Unfortunately, it sounded more like, "Tum on!" and "Yet doe adain," but she was *doing* it. She was putting herself out there and *really* talking.

Ashlynn had the biggest smile as she got off the slide and called to her friend to do it again. My heart swelled with happiness at seeing my daughter do what so many other children and parents see every day—talking to a child her age. However, that feeling disappeared quickly when the little girl asked her, "Are you a baby?"

My heart stopped for a second. Ashlynn, looking confused, just covered her eyes and laughed at her. On the sidelines, my heart broke. How *dare* this child say that!!! Didn't she know how much it took for my daughter to put herself out there and talk?

Of course, the rational side of me realized this girl was just a kid who didn't intend to be mean, but the mommy in me wanted to snap at her. Instead, as usual, Ashlynn was the role model. Her response to the girl was simply a laugh. Ashlynn has this incredible emotional intelligence and has always found clever ways of getting around her difficulties. She has never let anything or anyone stop her from living her life. So rather than feeling hurt by this girl, she just laughed it off.

It was during this year, at age four, that Ashlynn also told us her first "favorite." It might not seem much to someone without a child with apraxia, but kids are asked their favorite anything pretty much from the time they start talking. What is your favorite color? Which is your favorite animal at the zoo? What is your favorite candy? What is your favorite TV show, movie, toy, food, dessert, etc.? if Ashlynn has ever been partial to anything, we have never known, until one February weekend.

We went on a mini vacation at a local hotel. There was a pool and a hot tub, and it was next to many kid-friendly attractions, like the Cheyenne Mountain Zoo. As we returned to the hotel, my husband and

I kept asking Ashlynn questions: "What was your favorite animal, Ashlynn?" "Did you have fun?" "What was your favorite part?" She didn't really answer. But as we got closer to the hotel, she inquired, "Where we goin'?" We answered, "Back to the hotel." That's when we heard her first favorite anything. "Yes? That hotel's my favorite!"

My husband laughed and verified, "That hotel's your favorite?"

"Yeah!" she replied.

He turned to me and said aloud what I was already thinking, "That was the first time she's ever said anything was her favorite!" I don't think many parents with typically developing kids remember their first favorite anything, but moments like these are etched into our memories.

Toward the end of Ashlynn's second year in preschool, progress really started to pick up. She started to get in trouble for talking too much! I can't tell you how surreal it was to hear she needed to be told to be quiet. I know I should have been mad, but I cheered inside. My baby girl was finding her voice.

Every month they did a "show and share"; Ashlynn loved to share but would have to be coached by her SLP to participate—and this was after we had practiced a lot at home. Then, on the day of her show and share, I would send the questions and answers in her backpack and the SLP would help coach her. However, a note came home one day that said Ashlynn started talking about her items without needing the questions or any coaching.

I couldn't believe it. Sometimes it didn't feel like it was all really happening. All those months I spent in grief and fear, and now I finally had hope.

CHAPTER 8

Progress and Changes

Endings or beginnings,

depends on what you see.

I see the end, you see the start,

of something yet to be.

Every parent knows when something doesn't feel right and I started getting that feeling about eight months after working with Ashlynn's first private SLP. So, after much consideration, I made the decision to discontinue Ashlynn's speech therapy with her.

Primarily, I felt her therapy style did not meet Ashlynn's needs. She would have my three-and-half year old daughter sit in a chair across from her the entire time. The first fifteen minutes the speech therapist would do Kaufman cards; the last 15 minutes she would play with a fun toy and have my daughter request and comment on it. However, the session was very controlled. My daughter couldn't hold the toy and had to play with it only the way the SLP requested.

After a few more months of this, my daughter was over it. The first fifteen minutes of cards stretched to twenty and then twenty-five minutes. Apraxia therapy can be intense, but Ashlynn's SLP should have gotten more creative to get better results. Instead, if the therapist didn't get something accomplished during therapy time, she just told me to do it at home. I informed her that as a school based SLP (at the time), I didn't have the luxury of doing homework with Ashlynn. Kids need to be having fun, and that's how they learn the best. I learned later that appropriate therapy for apraxia should always, first and foremost, inspire and support a child's motivation. It is essential that children are motivated to achieve.

My mentor, Deborah Comfort, taught me that kids make so much more progress when they are engaged and having fun. Her therapy plans usually included three to four different activities in one thirty-minute session. The task would be multisensory in nature, methods that involve using any sensory and motor input available to enhance verbal skills. This usually involves some type of play activity that might, for example, have kids throwing a bean bag, walking like a crab, or even using felt and Velcro boards while engaged in speech tasks.

David Hammer, a well-known apraxia expert from Pittsburgh, does this as well. He has kids participating in puppet shows, shooting cards with a Nerf gun after they say their target syllable or sound sequence, or tossing bean bags in and out of a huge dinosaur's mouth. He has them banging on drums to represent each syllable in their word attempts This is the way to promote carryover, and I could see Ashlynn's SLP wasn't going to be the type of therapist to try alternative approaches. She may have known the Kaufman method well, but her therapy style wasn't what Ashlynn needed and was no longer producing results.

Remediation approaches for reading, math, and speech are always going to be out there and marketed to parents. It's important to note though that the facilitator of these programs play a big, if not bigger, part in helping the child progress. You can have the best program in the world, but if the child isn't motivated to do it or the therapist's style isn't a good match for the child, it won't work.

Ashlynn's SLP also kept expressing concern that my daughter didn't seem to be retaining memory of the words they worked on. I remember thinking that many of the target words held absolutely no meaning to Ashlynn—like "tuna," "tuba," and "oboe." I couldn't understand why learning these words was such a big deal if my daughter didn't come across them in her daily life.

In addition, the speech therapist seemed to have difficulty dealing with children and seemed so judgmental. I remember one day Ashlynn was having a hard time and throwing a temper tantrum. She was three. This SLP, who had no children of her own, smiled and then said, "My kids are going to hate me one day because I will never let them do that." I wanted to tell her that I was the perfect mother before I had actual kids with actual problems, but I let it go. Still, all these factors led me to finally realize that this SLP, though described as an expert at CAS therapy, wasn't the right fit for my daughter or our family.

When I was an assistant SLP, I worked under a lot of supervisors and was able to see a lot of different therapy styles. All therapists are qualified and trained professionals that will most likely get the job done; some just get the job done a lot faster. That's the kind of SLP I strive to be, and that's the type of speech therapist that my mentor was.

Many parents wonder how best to "break up" with their SLP. There really isn't one way of doing it. In our case, I just emailed Ashlynn's SLP one day and thanked her for all that she had done but told her that I was switching Ashlynn to my longtime friend and mentor for my daughter's speech therapy. I thought about telling the speech therapist the real reason why I left but decided against it. I had tried to tell her so many times, in so many ways, that I needed her to do something different, and there was no point in trying again.

After switching Ashlynn to Deborah (my own mentor) I immediately started seeing progress again. For example, about one to two months after the switch of speech therapists, my family was on the way to my parent's house to drop off the kids. The entire ride there, Ashlynn was talking about "Papa's house." When we rounded the corner of their street she announced, "Ashlynn happy. Ashlynn Papa's house. Ashlynn play ball Papa's house."

Previously, Ashlynn had told me she was happy only when I asked her if she was happy, or if we were reading a book about characters who were happy. I had never heard her say out of the blue and perfectly in context that she was happy and then tell me why she was happy.

Ashlynn's language bursts didn't stop there. A month later, our family went on our annual trip to Glendo State Park in Wyoming. When we got to the beach, Ashlynn saw my husband pull up on the jet ski. She looked at her grandpa and me and announced, "Ashlynn play boats with Daddy?" I teared up immediately. Hearing her put novel words together in context was such a wonderful feeling. We still had a long way to go, but these moments filled my heart with so much hope.

Children may get really good at saying things in the therapy session, but the transfer to saying them spontaneously in different environments may take much longer. This generalization piece is very difficult for kids with apraxia, which is why it requires a team approach that includes the parents who can carry over targets in many different environments to affect the best outcome. Along with speech growth, other great developments were happening for Ashlynn. All the work in occupational therapy and physical therapy was really paying off.

At Ashlynn's preschool picnic to celebrate the last day of school, the teacher brought out the trampoline—the same one that, a half a year earlier, Ashlynn could only march on. Well, this day, my daughter stood in line with that same big smile, that same beautiful energy, and when it was her turn, she got up on that trampoline *without* anyone's help, and she jumped and she jumped and she jumped some more. And when it was time to get off, she got down *without* anyone's help.

As I sat on the side watching, I realized that I was happy not just because my daughter could now jump. Really, I was so proud that despite being different and needing help to do many things, Ashlynn always *tried*. She tried with a smile and a giggle and her beautiful aura. She is always teaching me that life is what you make it; and when it's what you make it, **you will make it.**

Despite my daughter's success in different ways, in other areas she was still struggling. After a year of trying, Ashlynn still couldn't ride a tricycle. However, she had made progress and could now keep her feet straight on the pedals. She still couldn't figure out the actual alternating pushing motion. You'd think she would have been frustrated, but the opposite was true. As kids whizzed by on their bikes, Ashlynn happily laughed, giggled, and asked me, "See bicycle, Mama?" and then with determination in her face, she would get on her tricycle again, ready to practice. Like most other motor tasks, this one, too, would take time. In this journey with Ashlynn, I learned success was never really about the outcome, just as riding a bike is never really about the destination. Every bike rider will tell you the fun is found in the sights seen, the hills climbed, and, even possibly, the falls taken. Ashlynn, likewise, found her joy in the journey not just in the destination.

Ashlynn amazed me and continues to amaze me every day. I still hated that she had apraxia. I still hated that it seemed like she had to scratch and crawl for every achievement she made, but I started to realize and believe she would *always* do anything she set her heart to doing.

CHAPTER 9

Finding Our People

I am blessed to understand what it is like to have a child with apraxia.

I am blessed that I was chosen to be her mommy because, through her, I learned the true meaning of perseverance and bravery.

I am blessed because we have so many people in her corner.

I am blessed because out of the struggle came joys I could never have dreamed of or experienced myself.

I am blessed because though her diagnosis could have brought distance between my husband and me, it only brought us closer with the common goal of beating it.

I am blessed because, if not for her, I wouldn't have

set a goal to specialize in apraxia, and in turn, I may not have met all the wonderful people in my life or been able to treat all the wonderful children I see.

I am blessed because I never took for granted one word, one sentence, or one song.

I am blessed because I knew other parents who felt the same.

I am blessed because apraxia taught me gratitude.

I am blessed from simply being her mother.

This journey with Ashlynn through life has been one full of unexpected turns, steep inclines, and deep valleys. Though she and I traveled together, we took different roads. Ashlynn has always stayed positive, persevered, and, in the process, developed an amazing resilience. I, on the other hand, have vacillated between grief and acceptance, fighting and cheering. Many times, it was a lonely road, as it felt like no one could understand what I was going through.

I was thankful to stumble upon the Apraxia Kids Facebook group early on, where I could talk to other parents and have my experiences heard and validated.

Though it was comforting to find a support group and relate to other parents, I had the added guilt of being an SLP. I felt that no one else could understand what is was like to have a job where I helped children speak all day but couldn't help my own daughter. That was until another SLP mom of a child with apraxia found me and messaged me. Relief flooded my body. She understood exactly how I felt. It was profoundly comforting, and we messaged nearly every day for a year. We ended up forming a small but mighty Facebook group that is just for SLP moms of children with apraxia. C. S. Lewis summed it up best, "Friendship is born at that moment when one person says to another, 'What? You too? I thought I was the only one.'"

I formed a Facebook group just for us, "SLP Mommy of Apraxia," and I smile each time a new person finds us and expresses relief at knowing other parents who are going through or who had gone through the same experience. I always tell parents to find support for themselves, in addition to support for their child. In connecting with others, I found the key to being happy in my life with my beautiful girl: gratitude.

Gratitude is the secret ingredient in life that separates those who are happy from those who are bitter. Life is this beautiful mix of joys and disappointments; it can be intensely sad but also beautiful. Happiness and heartache, love and hate, companionship and loneliness. None of us get through life unscathed. We all have a unique set of challenges we experience; however, life is not a competitive sport. We are all in this together and finding others who share our challenges makes us stronger.

Ashlynn's diagnosis of apraxia felt like the most crushing news in the world at the time. Though I am a firm believer in gratitude, it doesn't happen right away, and parents need time and grace to grieve a diagnosis at their own pace. Grief is not finite. It ebbs and flows. It is a continuous cycle of pain, sadness, and acceptance.

One year at an Apraxia National Conference, the founder of Apraxia Kids welcomed us and told us to relax because we were with "our people." It felt so profoundly comforting. None of the parents attending had to explain apraxia to anyone there. We didn't have to explain common comorbidities and we didn't have to apologize for being sad. We could simply be our authentic selves and we were surrounded by others who completely understood. There is complete peace in that. Most parents, when faced with their child's diagnosis for the first time, have very overwhelming feelings. They feel *alone*.

In my personal experience and talking to the parents of my young clients, that is always the initial reaction. However, it doesn't have to be permanent. Finding others walking our same path eases the burden and connects us through our shared humanity.

CHAPTER 10

Training

"If it's both terrifying and amazing, then you should definitely pursue it."
—Erada Svetlana

The summer after Ashlynn's speech explosion, I was excited to attend the Apraxia Kids National Conference in Denver. Even though my family was living paycheck to paycheck and the conference cost several hundred dollars, I knew I had to find a way to go. I don't believe in coincidences. The apraxia national conference coming to Denver so soon after my daughter was diagnosed meant something. I had to be there.

The experience of the conference was incredible, to say the least. I think, looking back, I can definitely say that the conference set me on a path that changed my life, the path to becoming an expert on CAS.

I was beyond thrilled to meet Sharon Gretz, the founder of CASANA (the former name of Apraxia Kids). What an incredible women and inspiration she had been to me, and she was so down to earth and humble when I met her. We swapped stories and I immediately felt a kinship with her. It was also amazing to meet her young adult son, who was preverbal at age three, and now was talking and taking photos at the conference. Sharon reported that her son was in college maintaining a 3.25 GPA. His story was so inspiring.

I also met apraxia national expert David Hammer. I learned that he was the SLP who treated Sharon's son after he was first diagnosed with apraxia. I marveled at the connection. Sharon was the founder of the largest nonprofit dedicated exclusively to apraxia and the families it affected, and David Hammer, renowned international expert, had been her son's SLP.

Sharon and I discussed the first child with apraxia I had seen, David, and how much the Apraxia Kids website had helped me at that time. We commiserated about the fact that therapy for apraxia isn't generally taught in graduate school and how it's so important to seek out SLPs who have had additional training beyond their postgraduate degree regardless of whether they consider themselves an expert. Sharon eventually went on to add a new feature to the Apraxia Kids website. The "Find a Professional" area gave parents a credible source to go to when looking for an SLP who has postgraduate knowledge.

Later, I attended a cocktail hour and I spotted Ruth Stoeckel at a nearby table. I went up to her, tapped her on her shoulder, and gushed about how thankful I was for her work, research, and articles on apraxia. Unlike Sharon, Ruth looked slightly unnerved but thanked me before returning to her glass of wine. Though not the most promising meeting, this would not be the last time I would encounter Ruth Stoeckel.

The breakout sessions at the apraxia conference were amazing. I started to realize though, that Ashlynn had much more going on than just apraxia and that I needed to learn more to be able to help her. From the conference, I learned that most kids with apraxia had additional challenges, often called "comorbidities," and that rarely did apraxia occur in isolation. As I listened to terms mentioned in the conference sessions like dyspraxia, sensory processing disorder, ADHD, dyslexia, learning disabilities, executive functioning, and others, I started to realize I needed to have Ashlynn tested for more of these things. It was after this conference that I decided to pursue private occupational therapy for her, and I'm so thankful I did.

Everyone who was anyone in the field of CAS was at the Apraxia National Conference. Nancy Kaufman spoke on how to implement her Kaufman method (K-SLP), which was what Ashlynn had experienced those first nine months in private therapy after her diagnosis. I learned so much more about many of the fundamental techniques and practices that Kaufman felt were essential components in therapy for apraxia. I was also relieved to hear her say that the goal wasn't for the children to memorize her Kaufman cards, rather the child's motor plans were more important. Nancy Kaufman said children could go their entire life not knowing the word "oboe" (one of the images on a Kaufman card) and be just fine. I recalled Ashlynn's first SLP who had been concerned Ashlynn wasn't remembering these words, and I felt at peace with my decision to leave that therapist when we did.

At the end of the conference, I learned about the Apraxia Kids Intensive Training Institute for SLPs. This was a four-day professional training in all things apraxia, taught by leading apraxia experts. I decided this would be the next step in my goal of becoming an expert on apraxia. I asked Sharon Gretz, the founder of the National Apraxia organization about applying for the bootcamp, and though she said it was a competitive program, Sharon urged me to try. I decided I was going to start gaining more experience with apraxia and started networking with other colleagues. I was excited for what the future might bring.

After attending the conference, my desire to raise awareness about apraxia intensified. The more I learned about apraxia, the angrier I became that, despite a bachelor's and master's degree in Speech-Language Pathology, I had been completely ill-equipped to treat apraxia. I was embarrassed and angry that I hadn't even recognized apraxia in my own child. I hate admitting that, but I wanted it to be a lesson and not a mistake.

I became more active on my blog, slpmommyofapraxia.com, and its complementary Facebook page. I wanted to do my part to give back and share with others what I had learned. During those days when Ashlynn was first diagnosed, I had scoured the internet for blogs and information. I desperately wanted to find stories of others who had "beat" apraxia. And now I was determined that Ashlynn was going to be one of those success stories for others.

I went on to write an article for the American Speech-Language-Hearing Association about the signs and symptoms of apraxia. Not all children with apraxia will have all the signs, including "soft signs" like gross and fine motor skill delays. However, many will, and if they do, it *points* to apraxia even more. I had *never* learned this. *Never*.

I started to get angry. To me it didn't matter if apraxia was a supposedly rare disorder. There needed to be more awareness around this. If I, a practicing SLP, missed it in my own child, how may children are consistently getting overlooked nationwide? It doesn't matter if it's rare when it's *your* child that has it. The experts in speech should, at the very least, know how to identify it and then treat it.

I wrote blog post after blog post on my website with the goal of spreading awareness. The more I talked to parents, the more I realized just how little information there was about the diagnosis and treatment of apraxia. The judgment I heard from SLPs to parents was appalling. For example, some SLPs would tell the parents that they didn't read enough to their child, practice enough, or didn't do the speech homework. Many professionals seemed to even blame the parents for their child's lack of progress instead of recognizing that apraxia is a beast of a speech disorder, and maybe they, the professionals, weren't providing the right treatment. My passion for apraxia awareness grew from a flame to an inferno.

I was accepted into the Apraxia Kids Intensive Training Institute (aka Apraxia Bootcamp). I was excited and scared and worried that I would fail. But every morning I woke up and saw my daughter attack every task—speech, school, motor skills, etc.—with a smile on her face and an intense determination, and I would ask myself, "What is your excuse?"

The intensive training was in Pittsburgh. I arrived at the Pittsburgh airport and immediately saw David Hammer, one of my mentors. A year ago, I was telling him my story about how I found his articles on the Apraxia Kids website, and now here he was waiting for me and offering to give me a ride to the hotel.

Once at the institute, we participants were separated into three groups, each assigned to a specific mentor. The mentor of my group was Ruth Stoeckel. It was at her conference that I attended as a young SLPA that I began to suspect apraxia in my client David, during my first year as an SLP. I marveled at the fact that apraxia seemed to have chosen me and now here I was working to become an expert in it.

CHAPTER 11

Private Practice

*I'm angry that a mom went through this once.
I'm angry because a mom and child were going
through this again.
I'm angry because a mom and her child will go
through this in the future.
I'm angry because for every awareness success
story, I felt like I heard twice as many failures.
I'm angry because it wasn't just professional, it
was personal.*

The Apraxia Kids Training Institute fully equipped me to help my daughter—and other kids with childhood apraxia of speech. Not only did I know this disorder well from a parent's perspective, I was now a professional expert in treating it in other children.

My experience with Ashlynn equipped me in the best way possible to help my clients and future clients with CAS. Parents often carry a tremendous amount of guilt when their child doesn't speak. They are sensitive to the whispers and the questions. There is this unspoken assumption that when a child isn't speaking, it means the parents weren't as involved. Many educators, therapists, and parents may be familiar with a widely cited study done by the researchers Hart and Risley that concluded that a child's early family experience or lack thereof, is linked to their vocabulary and intellectual capability later in life. The stigma from this still lingers. But it has nothing to do with apraxia.

As an SLP and as her parent, I tried all sorts of tips and tricks with Ashlynn, but I didn't have the magic spell to help her speak or improve her other motor skills. Despite nightly therapy sessions, it seemed the one child I couldn't teach to talk was the one child that I wanted to help more than anyone in the world. The Hart and Risley study hung over my conscience like a black cloud.

Despite throwing myself into research, attending conference after conference on early intervention, and consulting with my colleagues, my daughter *still* struggled to speak. Though Ashlynn's articulation had drastically improved and she could speak in longer sentences, sometimes it seemed like she forgot that she could speak and would clam up when asked a direct question. There were times, too, that it seemed we took one step forward but then two steps back. Watching my child work harder than anyone else to say words and then lose those words was heartbreaking.

I've come a long way in this journey, but my guilt and feelings of failure were so strong that I went on an exhaustive mission to specialize in the disorder. I thought that at least if I were a specialist, I could truly believe and know that I did everything I could to help her.

I have finally come to terms with the fact that nothing I could have done would have made my daughter talk on the "typical" timetable. I also know that most parents are desperately doing everything they can to help their children. And I know that these parents often need emotional support when they bring their children in for therapy.

We speech therapy professionals need to be supporting parents just as much as we provide support to the children. I am now more conscious about how I deliver test scores and diagnoses. As a parent it can feel like a punch in the gut when you hear or read there is something wrong with your child. Some parents hide it well; some wear their heart on their sleeve. Regardless, I know how it feels to hear your child has a lifelong neurological disorder, and I try to approach it every time with honesty but also with compassion and empathy.

After the Apraxia Intensive Training Institute, I started my private practice to specialize exclusively in childhood apraxia of speech. Though excited about this direction in my professional life, each evaluation seemed to bring a story that would anger me. In one evaluation, the mom reported that a previous early-intervention SLP threw out the word "apraxia" in a flip way, as if it were nothing. It was only after this mother had googled the term months later, that she realized apraxia was a serious diagnosis that some individuals never fully overcome. The mom was upset about the disservice done to her daughter, but also mad about the potential disservice to other clients of this SLP.

I defended the SLP, saying I might not have realized how serious the diagnosis was early on in my career either. I stressed that *this* is the exact reason awareness is so important and that we must do our best to educate others about it.

Another mother I talked to was frustrated because two separate SLPs had told her that her daughter did not have apraxia. This mother continued to research apraxia and bring it up to the SLPs, but they dismissed her concerns each time. Desperate and looking for answers, the mom stumbled upon my blog and decided to drive two hours and pay out of pocket for a speech evaluation from me. She told me her daughter sounded very similar to Ashlynn.

Though the girl was very young (age two and a half), she cooperated fully with a speech articulation test and a motor speech evaluation. Despite knowing that an apraxia diagnosis before age three is usually done provisionally, I had more than enough support to diagnose childhood apraxia of speech rather than just suspected childhood apraxia of speech(sCAS). My report was so thorough that anyone who read it would at least be compelled to treat it as sCAS. When I told the mother my diagnosis she almost cried and said incredulously, "You believe me?"

I felt so bad. This poor mother. She knew more than the professionals treating her child. She had tried to tell those professionals what her daughter did at home, but the mother always felt dismissed. I wrote my report as explicitly as possible in the hope that the treating SLPs would change their therapy approach. Unfortunately, that wasn't the case.

"I don't think it's as dire as she made it seem. I still don't think it's apraxia," said one SLP.

The mother was beside herself. She felt defeated. There were no other SLPs in her area who took Medicaid, and the two SLPs treating her daughter refused to acknowledge the diagnosis of CAS.

When I am evaluating a child to determine a differential diagnosis for a speech problem, I find that, in reality, I am differentiating between a phonological disorder and apraxia. To put it simply, children with a phonological disorder may also have extremely unintelligible speech. They may have numerous sound errors, sound omissions, and sound distortions that make them very difficult to understand. However, their errors usually follow predictable patterns. For example, a child may delete all final consonants as a pattern or produce all /k/ sounds as /t/ sounds. When asked to produce a difficult word more than once, even if they don't produce the word correctly, they will most likely produce it the same way each time.

For example, a child with phonological disorder might be given the word "telescope" and be asked to repeat it five times. The child may have numerous errors and produce it as "teyecope," but regardless of how many times they say it or if they say it in a sentence, they will most likely continue to produce it as "teyecope." However, a child with apraxia who is engaged in the same task of repeating a word that is difficult for their speech motor system will frequently produce the same word differently each time, or if they put the word into a phrase or sentence, may omit more sounds from the word and make more errors.

Another example I like to use is a child whom I was treating who was "fronting," meaning he was producing sounds that should be produced in the back of the oral cavity, like /k/ and /g/, in the front of the oral cavity and substituting a /t/ and /d/. During a game of memory where I let the client take another turn if a match is produced, he excitedly shouted "I det to doe adain!" For this child, a /d/ was produced for every /g/ sound regardless of context or position in a word. In contrast, a parent of a child with apraxia may observe that the child can say a /t/ sound in "hot" but be unable to produce an initial /t/ sound as in "tea."

To complicate things even more, apraxia and phonological disorder are not necessarily mutually exclusive. In fact, as the child's apraxia component (speech motor planning) starts to resolve, a phonological disorder may be unmasked. We say "unmasked" because apraxia does not turn into a phonological disorder. Instead, sometimes the speech motor planning problem of apraxia hides a coexisting, underlying phonological problem.

In addition, many kids with resolving apraxia may progress to demonstrating only one to three speech sound errors, and in that apraxia a label of articulation disorder may be more appropriate.

I kept thinking that if there was just more awareness and education, things would improve for these kids. I racked my brain, wondering how to get people to actually hear the message. I had no idea the attention apraxia was about to get.

CHAPTER 12

Her Fight, Our Fight

"I never would have been able to do any of those things without hope. The kind of hope I'm talking about is the belief that something good will come. That everything you're going through and everything you've gone through will be worth the struggles and frustrations. The kind of hope I'm talking about is a deep belief that the world can be changed, that the impossible is possible."
—Ronda Rousey

With each new client, my passion for apraxia and awareness grew. I kept thinking how great it would be to find someone in the public eye who had apraxia and beat it. How inspiring that would be for our community.

My hope turned into reality after I read an article on MMA fighter and actor Ronda Rousey. The description of her speech difficulties as a child read like a case history for childhood apraxia of speech. So significant was her so-called speech impediment that her parents moved from California to North Dakota so she could attend intensive speech therapy sessions.

After reading the article, I researched her early history exhaustively. Stories about her as a child would sound so familiar to any apraxia parent. For example, one time her dad took her to the toy store but couldn't understand what she was asking for. He made the store clerk show them every item until they finally figured it out: An Incredible Hulk doll. I just knew Ronda probably had apraxia. I had to at least ask.

I met Ronda at a book signing. She hadn't heard of apraxia, so I gave her an informational brochure, which she then read and reposted on her Twitter feed, spreading awareness to her millions of followers. In a *Good Morning America* interview the following year, she described reading the brochure I had given her and how it helped her realize that apraxia was exactly what she had had.

Ronda has since gone on to say she had apraxia in other interviews and on the TV show *Battle of the Network Stars*. She even showed up at Los Angeles's Walk for Apraxia in 2017 and gave a medal to all the kids with apraxia walking to find their voice. The awareness that spread from having a celebrity of her stature talk about apraxia has been immeasurable.

Ronda is a living, breathing symbol of hope for the apraxia community. She speaks beautifully in interviews with barely a hint of apraxia. We can all find hope in her story that one day our child who struggles to speak can be successful in life.

Unfortunately, there is an ugly side. The truth is, it's not easy and some children will not beat apraxia. A child with apraxia is not your typical late talker. Apraxia is a hard-wired neurological problem that only has a chance of being remediated by intense and appropriate speech therapy; and ideally this therapy needs to be early, when the brain has the most plasticity.

It was only because of Ronda's mother, AnnMaria, and her unwavering commitment to her daughter, that I believe Ronda overcame apraxia. Professionals in their home state of California told her mother she would eventually speak, but AnnMaria knew in her gut that was wrong. Despite professionals reassuring her that Ronda would be fine, she trusted her intuition and moved her family from California to North Dakota. She accepted a job at a university where Ronda would be able to receive *intense* and *frequent* speech therapy. That was a huge but, I believe, necessary sacrifice.

AnnMaria commented on my blog post that she often wonders what would have happened had her daughter not received that therapy. My response was that Ronda may have still been the world's best MMA fighter, but she would not be speaking as well as she does today. That is the **reality** of apraxia. I tell people all the time that even though I'm an SLP specializing in the disorder, my daughter *still* sees a private SLP in addition to her school SLP. This disorder requires that much therapy.

One summer I was trying a new hair stylist. I told her I was an SLP specializing in a severe speech disorder called "apraxia." She nonchalantly said her cousin had that. My eyebrows raised a little, but then she started describing her cousin's speech as that of about a toddler. I asked how old she was, and she replied, "Sixteen."

My stomach immediately turned into knots. I learned that her parents had only ever had the child in school therapy. School therapy is not bad but let me remind you that I am an SLP and my daughter still sees a private SLP. Apraxia may be a war you didn't sign up for, but you have been drafted and now you need to fight. If you want your child to beat this, you need to come out with every gun blazing and with every soldier at your disposal.

The story of Ronda and her mom inspired me to do everything I could to help Ashlynn, but also to continue to spread awareness in the hope of helping all children with apraxia get the appropriate diagnosis and services.

CHAPTER 13

Overcoming Apraxia

Little Ashlynn, little Ashlynn,

She's my little Ashlynn girl.

And I love her, yes, I love her more than anything in the world.

She's my baby.

She is pretty.

Ashlynn is my pretty girl.

And I love her, yes, I love her more than anything in the world.

When Ashlynn was around four, family began understanding her better, but others still questioned what she was saying. I knew what she was saying

99 percent of the time, so it was disheartening when even her school SLP rated Ashlynn's speech at about 60 percent intelligibility. This was disappointing, but the honest feedback was helpful and necessary.

However, Ashlynn kept making progress and the light at the end of the tunnel started becoming brighter and brighter. She went from not being able to say anything during "show and share" at school to saying one to two words in front of the entire class without the SLP's help!

She also learned to say her name, articulating every sound; I have the moment recorded on video. Back when Ashlynn was first learning how to string simple sounds into basic syllables, her SLP had her practice "Ash-in." She had never tried to say her name before, but by scaffolding it back to a word approximation, she was finally willing to try and kept that version of her name for the next year and a half.

People would ask her, "What is your name?" My husband and I would wait for her to respond with the predictable, "Ashin." The person would then respond with the equally predictable, "Oh, hi, Ashley!" Then my husband or I would swoop in and clarify, "Yes, Ashlynn!"

But one day I heard her say a friend's name from class, Calista. I whipped my head around and pleaded for her to say it again. Same as before, she said a perfect /l/ sound in Calista.

"Ashlynn," I gushed, "do you realize that sound is in your name too? Let's try it! And on video, she was no longer "Ashin," but "Ashlynn."

During her last year of preschool, things really started clicking for her. Ashlynn could tell me what she learned in school. She told me that bears hibernate and that we lived in Colorado. Was this really the girl who, three years ago, couldn't speak enough to tell me what she had for lunch? I was so grateful.

On Ashlynn's fifth birthday though, I really started to notice big changes. I posted a video of her on social media, and the feedback was incredible. Everyone could understand her! Other people were validating what I had been seeing for so long! I could suddenly breathe again, and the future seemed clearer.

A progress note from school only listed a few residual articulation errors. Of more concern now was expressive language delays, including grammar and sentence formulation, and Ashlynn's crippling struggle with word finding. That's when it hit me. Ashlynn was almost resolved from apraxia. Her speech motor plans had caught up. Apraxia, in its truest sense, is just a problem with the programming and planning of speech movements. It does not include issues with grammar, syntax, or other language-based problems. My daughter still had a significant expressive/receptive language impairment, but her apraxia was resolving. Ashlynn from now on, would be able to speak intelligibly. That realization hit me like a smack in the face and sent my spirits soaring to the moon!

At Ashlynn's reevaluation the spring before she would start kindergarten, Ashlynn was administered a standardized test, the Goldman Fristoe Test of Articulation 2. In special education, children are given two types of assessments: standardized and criterion referenced. A standardized test refers to an assessment with questions that have been norm-referenced across a sample of children the same age, allowing comparison of the child being tested to the other children who took the same test. A criterion-referenced test refers to an assessment that is not norm-referenced to the other same-aged children, but rather looks at a particular skillset or criterion that a child should have by a certain age or grade level.

Standardized assessments are typically used for determining whether a child is eligible for special education. Different test instruments may vary somewhat, but usually, standard scores of 85 to 115 are considered within the average range. Ashlynn received a standard score of 86 on the Goldman Fristoe, indicating articulation performance within the low average range. I didn't even see the word "low." My daughter with apraxia, after two years of intense speech therapy, was now in the average range on a standardized articulation measurement!

I once read somewhere that the days are long, but the years are short. It's true. At some point I had stopped praying that Ashlynn would overcome apraxia, but I couldn't recall exactly when that was. I reflected on the fact that in just two short years, Ashlynn's apraxia was resolving, I met the head of Apraxia Kids, gained advanced training and expertise in apraxia, and now had my own private practice specializing in the disorder. I remembered being a sobbing mess the day of Ashlynn's initial diagnostic evaluation, and I could never have dreamed the events that would take place in the ensuing years.

Even though I was late to the game (because I so wanted to believe Ashlynn was just a late talker), none of this would have been possible without early and *appropriate* intervention. I'm so grateful that Ashlynn's initial evaluating SLP in the school told me it was CAS. Rather than spinning my wheels providing treatment that wasn't appropriate for apraxia, I knew to change the treatment plan and get her private services. I knew at that point that I had to research this disorder. I knew then that our life would never be the same. I knew the potential consequence if we didn't change our treatment approach.

Therapy can be expensive, but it's worth it. I used the money I had saved for my maternity leave for my son to pay for Ashlynn's private therapy. We made sacrifices. I knew I didn't want Ashlynn walking into a kindergarten classroom nonverbal, so my husband and I did what we had to do and nearly went broke funding her therapy. Luckily, there are a variety of grant programs, community center board programs, and even Medicaid programs that can help children who need additional therapy, including United Health Care Children's Foundation, Small Steps in Speech, Scottish Right Foundation, Easter Seals, Medicaid, Katie Beckett Waiver, and Community Centered Boards.

However, although Ashlynn's apraxia had resolved, her journey with speech was not yet over.

CHAPTER 14

Additional Characteristics

Light peeking in the distance,
we forged forward.

Hand in hand and side by side,
we marched to it.

Brighter and brighter it grew,
We raised up our faces.

Warmer and warmer it shone,
we smiled wider.

Early on, I had assumed that once Ashlynn's apraxia improved, everything would be fine. But that was not to be the case. Ashlynn was still struggling to master basic functional communication skills that were intelligible to the everyday listener. In addition, kids with apraxia of speech can have difficulty initiating speech. I have parents report all the time that though children may say words in therapy, they do not say them at home unless prompted. This has implications for their ability to produce longer sentences, since they may still be struggling with the motor task of starting a sequence.

The earliest example of difficulties with initiation for Ashlynn started with the word "Mama." When Ashlynn was born, I remember competing with my husband to see if she'd say "Mama" or "Dada" first. I was with her more and I was a speech-language pathologist so I was pretty sure I would win. Little did I know then, there are no winners when your child has apraxia.

Days turned into weeks, and weeks turned into months, and months gave way to at least a year, and I never heard her say my name. Not hearing your baby say "Mama" or some version of "Mama" around their first birthday breaks your heart into pieces.

Every morning I would go into her room, coo and talk to her, and ache to hear her say, "Mama." When she could finally hold up her arms to request for me to hold her, I knew it was me she wanted to see, but her voice remained locked up inside her.

Finally, in speech therapy, she was able to imitate and then produce those sweet two sounds and say, "Mama." I assumed that was it. She could finally say it and she would call to me from now on.

She didn't.

Though she was able to repeat it numerous times in speech therapy, when she didn't receive cues or prompts from her SLP, she could only smile, wave her arms, and giggle. No "Mama."

The same phenomenon happened with the phrase "I love you." These words are cherished by any parent. These words are eagerly anticipated. When you have a child with a speech delay, the eager anticipation eventually gives way to desperation and sometimes even apathy.

Ashlynn had been able to say, "I love you," when it was modeled for her. Once she really got good at imitating, we had her imitate it every time we told her good night and tucked her into bed. As she grew older, she automatically said it after we said it in any situation. We were happy. However, she would say it only after hearing the model first, not spontaneously. One day though, I finally heard those words from her first. She said them in a moment of pure joy, and I felt so blessed.

It happened over summer break. Ashlynn loved art and loved making messes. I'm a writer. Writing is so clean. A pen and paper are all you need to create beauty out of words, which then are easily put away until later. Young kids love a good mess, especially those with any type of executive functioning difficulties.

Ashlynn begged to do messy things. She loved the tactile sensory input. She would play with modeling clay, and it would end up everywhere, including her hair, her shoes, and the carpet. My mantra became, "Let it go, Mama."

I would let her play with water in the sink. A few minutes later the water would inevitably end up in a huge puddle all over the counter, the floor, her shirt, her pants. "Let it go, Mama," I would say to myself.

I would let her play in the dirt outside. However, the dirt somehow happened to turn into mud that would get under her fingernails, in her shoes, on her shirt, and somehow ground into the carpet. "Let it go, Mama," I would repeat in my head.

One day I was at the grocery getting some odds and ends. I'm not generally an impulse shopper, but I noticed the dollar bins and decided to take a peek.

I saw some foam stickers and was reminded of all the papers that had come home in Ashlynn's backpack full of scribbles and foam stickers. I didn't understand the purpose; you put them on paper and then throw the paper away. What's the point? But I remembered how much joy they brought Ashlynn and recalled that they can be good for bilateral hand coordination since you need both hands and fine motor control to get the paper off the back; I bought them.

I brought them home and she was happy. Not overly happy, but happy. She was busily creating when she randomly walked over to me and tapped me on the leg. "Mama, Mama, MAMA!!" she said.

"What, honey?"

"I love you!!"

I was stunned, not understanding what had prompted the utterance. That's when I looked a few feet beyond her to the messy table, the backs of foam stickers littering my carpet, and paper after paper full of foam stickers. I gave her the biggest hug. I might have cried. She had found a way to tell me how much those messy stickers meant to her, without telling me that at all. She saved her first spontaneous "I love you" for the occasion.

Sometimes a child may be able to initiate a motor plan but get "stuck" in one. For example, when Ashlynn would spend all day with my mother-in-law, she would come home and call me "Grandma." She would do this even though she knew I was Mama. When I asked her if I was Grandma, she would laugh and shake her head no. Since Ashlynn has an additional developmental language disorder, her ability to express herself with language, even as her apraxia resolved, remained severely impaired.

"Developmental language disorder" (DLD) is the current accepted term, but it has also been referred to as "specific language impairment," "language disorder," and "mixed expressive/receptive language disorder." With all the different terms, it's easy for parents to be confused. To add to the confusion, children can just have an expressive language disorder in which the receptive language is average, but expressive language skills are impaired.

Children with a language impairment can struggle with various skills involving the understanding or use of spoken language. These can include things like a smaller vocabulary, impaired grammar and syntax formulation, word-finding difficulties, and difficulty comprehending spoken language, just to name a few. Not all kids with speech apraxia will have a language disorder and not all kids with a language disorder will present with the same profile of skills. In my practice, I have clients ranging from a mild expressive language disorder with just a few grammar and syntax errors to clients who have more severe impairment of both receptive and expressive language skills.

An example of how DLD affected our family happened one evening when our family had gone to dinner, and I spent most of it in the bathroom with Ashlynn. She kept thinking she had to go "potty." We walked around, we jumped, we danced, but nothing happened. She started saying she was tired, which is unusual for her. I asked her if she felt sick. She said no.

We drove home, gave her a bath, and she went straight to bed. I rubbed her back and asked her again if she felt sick. Did she feel like she was going to throw up? Did her tummy hurt? She just shook her head no.

I went out to the living room, and not five minutes later, I heard her coughing and then throwing up. It was a glaring reminder of how learning to speak intelligibly did not fix everything. She still struggled to connect vocabulary with her experiences, likely due to her language disorder.

I learned through this journey with Ashlynn that finding one's voice can be more complicated than just learning how to sequence speech sounds correctly. I really understood—now from the parental perspective—just how much a communication disorder really affects a child in everyday life. Since this time, Ashlynn's language skills have improved greatly, but processing and using language is still something she struggles with to this day. She continues to struggle to answer questions on demand that require an explanation. For example, one day I asked her if she liked having apraxia and she responded, "No." When I asked her why, she took some extra processing time before finally giving up and saying, "I can't, Mommy."

Language is imbedded in all school subjects, and children like Ashlynn who have difficulty with processing language may need additional support. In school, skills such as retelling a story to include all the pertinent details also remain challenging. Things like following multi-step directions may need an accommodation to chunk directions and to provide frequent checks for comprehension. Visuals can be helpful, such as writing key points on the board as opposed to just stating them auditorily. Explicit instruction with comprehension may also be necessary.

Finally, it's important to mention that many

children with apraxia may struggle with some degree of semantic and word finding issues. This happened a lot when learning new skills in school. Despite knowing her colors, she would make expressive errors. For example, if I asked her what color her red shirt was, she might say, "purple," but when I followed up and asked her if it was purple, she would shake her head no. Because this happened so frequently, I had an accommodation put into her IEP that she be tested receptively (for example, she would be asked to point to red instead of being asked the name of the color) to get a more accurate picture of her true knowledge and abilities.

Children with word-finding difficulties may conceptually know a word but be unable to retrieve it expressively in certain contexts. It's important that parents and speech language pathologists are aware of this so they can advocate for the child with apraxia to get the accommodations they might need. To complicate things further, the child with apraxia might be struggling with additional difficulties such as motor initiation or "getting stuck" in a familiar motor plan that could look like they don't have knowledge or a skill, but in fact are just struggling to expressively demonstrate their knowledge.

That does not mean that every child with apraxia will have a language disorder or struggle with language to the extent Ashlynn has either. However, I think it's good for parents to know the difference and be vigilant for any further issues and bring them up to the child's SLP when they have concerns. In an unpublished retrospective study of children with apraxia seen at Mayo Clinic, out of a group of 391 children given a diagnosis of apraxia by expert SLPs, only ten did not have a co-occurring diagnosis of language disorder.

CHAPTER 15

Specialists

Sometimes Bravery is loud,

with sharp swords and hard armor.

Sometimes Bravery is fearless,

demanding respect with each step.

Sometimes Bravery is strong,

with big muscles and powerful weapons.

However,

sometimes Bravery is quiet,

with soft words and a determined smile.

Sometimes Bravery is scared,

but still faces each day with new grit.

Sometimes Bravery is underestimated,

in small bodies but with determined spirit.

And,

the underestimated Bravery is my favorite,

because underestimated Bravery is YOU.

Ideally, after a diagnosis of apraxia, the pediatrician or other professional will recommend visiting specialists to determine, if possible, any underlying cause of the apraxia. Though in many cases, apraxia is idiopathic, of no known origin, apraxia *can be* caused by brain damage or an abnormality that happened in utero or right after birth. Some parents may find themselves referred to a developmental pediatrician, a neurologist, or a geneticist.

Developmental Pediatrician

I first found out about developmental pediatricians and how they differ from regular pediatricians through the Apraxia Kids support group page on Facebook. Many parents talked about how their children with apraxia were followed by a developmental pediatrician, along with a regular pediatrician. When I asked my regular pediatrician for a referral, she simply said she could prescribe an MRI and some basic genetic testing, but I know now though that developmental pediatricians are specialists in developmental disorders and are the best professionals to follow a developmentally delayed child's progress and growth over time. In addition, developmental pediatricians can make informed referrals to other specialists a child might need to see, such as a neurologist, a neuropsychologist, a genetic doctor, and/or rehabilitation physician.

Neurologist

A neurologist treats children who have problems with the nervous system. This could include issues such as epilepsy, tics, and sleep disorders. In our case, a neurologist ordered an MRI to see if Ashlynn's apraxia was caused by some sort of brain damage or brain abnormality. In her case, the MRI came out negative, but I have heard of MRIs showing positive for cysts, demyelination, intrauterine stroke damage, extra fluid, or hypoplasia, a congenital malformation of the brain.

Neuropsychologist

A neuropsychologist is similar to a regular psychologist in that they both give IQ tests and look at a child's cognitive profile of strengths and weaknesses. However, a neuropsychologist has additional expertise in children with neurodevelopmental disorders and has more knowledge about how a child's specific disorder may or may not have influenced test results or performance.

Geneticist

These are specialist doctors who usually work with a genetic counselor. They order specific genetic tests that look at defects in the genes. In our case, the genetic doctor ordered a partial exome sequencing panel based on Ashlynn's presentation of symptoms. In Ashlynn's case, a mutation called BCL11A was discovered and is the reason for her constellation of disorders.

Rehabilitation Physician

This specialist looks at improving functional ability and quality of life to those with physical impairments or disabilities.

These doctors may or may not be covered by insurance, leading parents to wonder about the necessity of seeing them. After all, if we treat the symptoms and have children in the appropriate therapies, what is to be gained by knowing the cause? Is that knowledge worth the cost? That is one of the many difficult decisions a parent must make on the special-needs journey. Be cautioned though that just because doctors are specialists, it doesn't mean they are specialists on your child. It's up to parents to advocate for their children and their specific needs.

I took Ashlynn to a neurologist, assuming that neurologists have a clear understanding of apraxia since it is a neurological disorder. In this particular appointment, there was a resident doctor and supervising doctor. The supervisor came in to review the file and give Ashlynn one more exit exam. I knew the MRI and genetic testing ordered by Ashlynn's pediatrician hadn't yielded any helpful information. I was there to see what the neurology experts' diagnosis would be. Suddenly I heard the supervisor tell the resident that Ashlynn didn't have apraxia. I struggled to process what had been said.

"Excuse me. Did you just say she doesn't have apraxia or oral apraxia? Ask her to close her eyes on command. She can't. Ask her to spit out some water. She can't. Ask her to smile on demand. She can't. Ask her to blow her nose. She can't. Oh, and if you don't hear her apraxia, I can quickly take you through a motor speech exam."

The supervisor did many of the non-speech things I recommended. She saw, as I had said, Ashlynn couldn't do them. She then looked at her resident, again as though I wasn't in the room and commented, "Oh, is this the SLP?"

"Yes, I'm an SLP that specializes in her disorder," I responded for the resident. "Would you like me to take you through a motor speech exam?" I reiterated.

She told me that wasn't necessary and changed the subject to the next course of action. I was stunned. This neurologist had completely dismissed Ashlynn's diagnosis of apraxia, even knowing I'm a speech-language pathologist. I was angered. If she treated me with this disregard, how did she act to parents who weren't experts in apraxia?

They denied my request to put "apraxia" in their report. It was a hard lesson for me that just because we were seeing experts didn't mean they were experts on everything going on with my child. It reinforced what I already knew—that parents are the experts on their own children and have to be their best advocate.

CHAPTER 16

CEO/CFO of Special Needs Parenting

Going through my life,
adrift upon the seas,
Not knowing where I'm going,
at the mercy of the breeze.
I'd traveled to many places,
thought happiness I'd found.
So sure that I was living,
until you came around.

I like to tell parents that they are the experts on their own children. We might not understand every disorder or disease, but we know *them* like no one else can. I know what Ashlynn looks like before she starts choking, I know that she will start picking her nails when she is getting anxious, I know that slight quiver her bottom lip makes when she's trying not to cry. I know all of it, as other parents know everything about their children. That is why it is so important that professionals, all professionals, take the time to listen to what the parents say as part of a comprehensive evaluation.

It's so important for parents to educate themselves about CAS (and any comorbidities) and how best to advocate for their children. Knowledge is power.

Not only are we, as parents, experts on our children, we must be the chief executive officers (CEOs) of their care. The CEO, by definition, oversees all management decisions, and with children with unique needs, there is a lot to manage.

Some days, it does feel unmanageable. It feels like parents are responsible for the success of their *child's future*. The stakes are higher when you have a child with some sort of delay or disability. Children with special needs are already starting life at the back of the pack. As parents, we feel an intense responsibility to give them the best chance at a normal life, which is hard enough in this world even without a disability.

Parenting a child with special needs is a juggling act. When parents have a kid with special needs, they spend a lot of their time at the pediatrician, and often bounce from specialist to specialist just to get an actual diagnosis. They may have taken their children to neurologists and psychologists. Their kids have had blood taken and scans done, and then had more doctor visits to discuss results. Their kids have been poked, prodded, and examined more than their typical peers. Their tiny bodies might have been subjected to sleep studies, sedation, and, sometimes, surgery.

Therapy is always in the mix. Children with disabilities may see occupational therapists, physical therapists, speech therapists, play therapists, behavior therapists, early interventionists, and/or vision therapists. Seeing therapists always means more new evaluations, where children who already struggle are subjected to tests and judgements about their performance compared to typical peers.

Obviously, there are only so many hours in a day and so the CEO must prioritize specialists and therapies and activities. It can be excruciatingly difficult to decide which doctor or therapy your child needs most or more.

In addition, every single therapy has homework (in addition to homework from school). At one point, Ashlynn was going to speech therapy twice a week, occupational therapy (OT) twice a week, and tutoring once a week—and every one of the sessions had expectations for work we would complete at home. On one evening, Ashlynn got off school at 3:00, tutoring at 3:30, and OT at 5:00. By the time we got home at 6:30, we had a short time to eat dinner, leaving an hour before bedtime. In that hour, we needed to do her math, reading, and spelling homework from school, along with completing her nightly speech exercises and OT exercises.

She was eight years old.

Was I really going to expect my eight year old to work all day at school, go to tutoring and OT, and then in the one hour she had to just be a kid, force her to do her school homework, her speech and OT exercises, and run through her words from tutoring?

These are the decisions I had to make, and they were also decisions that caused judgmental frowns from therapists and teachers, who questioned politely, "You really can't fit in a quick fifteen minutes of homework?" These inquiries always made me feel like a failure, but really, they just didn't understand how packed Ashlynn's schedule was.

If you are a professional who is reading this, please take these words to heart. Please understand and assume that most parents are doing the very best they can because they probably are. Meet them there. You don't know what else they may be dealing with in their lives.

Let's not forget money. All these things cost *money*. Insurance in many cases does not cover the brain scans, the MRIs, the evaluations, and all the therapies. A parent must become the chief financial officer (CFO) for their child as well.

A CFO is responsible for the financial affairs. People don't plan on budgeting for the thousands of dollars it will cost to put their kids in therapy when they are setting up their budget for buying their first home and preparing for a baby. I had a supervisor tell me once at a private practice, *no one* knew to budget all the therapies, doctor appointments, and evaluations.

If you are lucky and receive some sort of disability aid or payment, Medicaid, or scholarship to help fund the cost, it's not without another price: time. All these applications for supplemental funding take an enormous amount of time.

To apply for supplemental funding, parents need to gather required documentation: letters from insurance companies and doctors, evaluations, tax returns, and medical records. A parent will spend hours filling out paperwork and, on the phone, to make appointments or get help with forms. This time is well spent if a parent can get insurance to cover a specialist or get money to help with expenses. However, finding the time is the hard part. When parents are not working, they are shuffling their kids to doctor appointments and therapy appointments and school, in addition to typical kid stuff like sports or birthday parties in the hopes that the child can feel normal for at least some of their childhood.

The mother—in my observation is usually the CEO/CFO, though not always—and this additional stress adds a huge emotional toll. In a study by Allen and Babin (2012), the researchers found that mothers of children diagnosed with speech impairments are at a greater risk for depression and more susceptible to experiencing psychosomatic symptoms including headaches, fatigue, and dizziness, in addition to an elevated level of anxiety. In another study done by Miron (2012), the researchers identified three phases mothers go through after a specific apraxia diagnosis. The first phase is characterized by fear, uncertainty, and helplessness.

It is a sad reality that many marriages struggle when there is a child with unique needs. Decisions on therapy, parenting, how to parent, and money are magnified even more. In some cases, moms can get so wrapped up in helping their children, they forget to put energy toward the marriage. In other instances, all their energy has been used up and they have no more to give. Some might feel resentful of their partner for not being available or involved like the mother thinks they should.

Fathers may be grieving too but might feel they have to be strong for their partner. They might also be grieving but may not be as likely to share their emotions for fear of not being strong for their partner.

Whatever the situation, it's important that couples recognize this and try and work together. Keep an open line of communication and try to be more compassionate and understanding of each other.

If we are lucky, there are times we CEO/CFO parents find the perfect team. We've got the diagnosis, the plan, and the team of therapists to treat it, and we see our child do the most amazing thing in the entire world: ***make progress.***

And we realize, all the guilt, all the stress, all the worry, all the money, and all the time was 100 percent worth it.

CHAPTER 17

The Big Picture

Over my career specializing in the disorder, I definitely feel apraxia is rarely the primary issue, rather a sequela to a bigger picture. The problem is SLPs and parents are so focused on the speech and not looking at the big picture in early development. There is this thinking that if we could just overcome the apraxia, everything will be okay.
—Lynn Carahaly, MS CCC-SLP

As a professional SLP specializing in speech apraxia, I have a private-practice caseload of around thirty-five kids. There is not one child who doesn't have another condition. I must repeat that because it is important. There is not *one* who *only* has apraxia.

Why? What does it matter? You take each diagnosis day by day, right?

Through my journey with Ashlynn, and now through my professional practice, I have discovered that if a child gets diagnosed with apraxia, it will rarely be the only diagnosis the child will go on to receive. That doesn't mean that pure apraxia doesn't exist. It does, but I haven't seen it in my career.

Apraxia, a neurological, verbal, motor-planning disorder, is frequently discovered and identified first in a child's life. However, a neurological disorder rarely is present in only one system in a child. When I was a school SLP, I sat through many an IEP meeting in which school OTs diagnosed children with motor-planning delays. Through this experience with Ashlynn, I realize just how many of those children probably had a version of dyspraxia, or developmental coordination disorder.

Some of the more common comorbidities with childhood apraxia of speech:

Developmental Language Disorder: Can refer to receptive language, expressive language, or both. Children with language disorders may have difficulty with word finding, vocabulary, grammar, and syntax.

Dysarthria: A motor speech disorder caused by

muscle weakness that can affect the clarity, precision, rate, and prosody of speech.

Oral Apraxia: A term used to describe difficulties with non-speech, oral motor movements of the mouth. May present itself as difficulty with puckering, smiling, or moving the tongue in various movements and positions on command.

Phonological and Articulation Disorders: Developmental speech disorders that affect the child's speech sound production. Phonological disorder is usually reserved for children who have a pervasive pattern of sound errors. Articulation disorder is a term used to reference those who have just a few sound errors.

Stuttering/Fluency Disorder: A neurological speech disorder characterized by breaks in the natural flow or fluency of speech, which may include repetitions, prolongations, and/or blocks.

Non-Speech Conditions

ADHD (Attention Deficit Hyperactivity Disorder): A term used to describe a neurologically based disorder in which an individual has difficulty attending to meaningful tasks. This may present as hyperactivity, inattention, and/or impulsivity.

Autism: A complex neurological condition typically characterized by difficulties with communication and a set of rigid or repetitive behaviors. Autism is a spectrum disorder.

Dyspraxia: Sometimes referred to as developmental coordination disorder, dyspraxia is a term used to describe a motor planning disorder that affects fine and/or gross motor coordination. Dyspraxia may affect handwriting and tasks of daily living, such as dressing and toileting.

Dyslexia: A neurological learning disability characterized by a deficit in the phonological component of language that affects spelling and decoding. Children with dyslexia need a multisensory, structured, and sequential method to reading instruction that includes phonics and phonics rules. It's important to know schools do not diagnose children specifically with dyslexia, but rather use an educational disability term.

Executive Functioning Disorder: Executive functioning skills are regulated by the prefrontal cortex in the brain. Many kids with developmental delays and neurodevelopmental disabilities such as apraxia, dyspraxia, autism, ADHD, and sensory processing disorder, are at a high risk for deficits with executive functioning skills. Executive functioning skills can be formally diagnosed by a psychologist. One such test is called the Behavior Rating Inventory of Executive Functioning (BRIEF). If you think your child might have issues with this, ask your school psychologist to test for it.

Reading Disorder: An umbrella term to describe any difficulty with reading. A reading disorder can result from dyslexia or be caused by other issues, including lack of fluency or poor reading comprehension.

Sensory Processing Disorder (SPD): Sometimes referred to as sensory integration dysfunction, SPD is not an officially recognized disorder in the DSM V; SPD is an umbrella term used to describe an abnormal response to sensory stimuli. Children vary greatly in their unique sensory profiles. The best person to consult when SPD is suspected is an occupational therapist.

Parents and professionals need to be aware of the common and potential comorbidities that can exist in children with apraxia so children can receive early intervention, if needed. In addition, knowledgeable professionals can make referrals as needed to other specialists who may be able to help.

Genetic Disorders

In an article written by Morgan and Webster (2018) for the *Journal of Pediatrics and Child Health*, the authors offered compelling data that in the cases of true and confirmed apraxia, pediatricians recommend pursuing genetic causes.

This current interest was catapulted by the discovery that a mutation on a gene called FoxP2 was implicated in both heritable (passed from parent to child) and *de novo* (new variant) causes of CAS up to almost 100 percent prevalence in affected individuals. Since that time, genetic testing has been increasingly pursued and recommended in children who have CAS or other neurodevelopmental disorders. The authors go on to discuss many other genetic disorders currently being implicated in CAS among other neurodevelopmental comorbidities such as:

16p.11.2: Associated with CAS, moderate cognitive disability, autism, epilepsy, language disorder, and dysarthria.

7q11.23 Duplication: Associated with delayed speech and motor skills.

GRIN2A: Associated with CAS, dysarthria, and oral-motor impairments

SETBP1: Associated with CAS, expressive language disorder (but intact receptive language disorder), decreased fine motor skills, ADHD, and autistic traits.

KANSL1: Associated with feeding difficulties, CAS, dysarthria, and hypotonia.

ELKS/ERC1: Associated with CAS, delayed walking, language and reading difficulties, intellectual impairments, psychiatric manifestations, and ADHD. ASD was diagnosed in some but had a low prevalence.

BCL11A: Associated with CAS, dysarthria, hypotonia, and general oral and gross motor dyspraxia.

These lists are not exhaustive; profiles of each disorder are not complete since the field of genetics is currently developing at a rapid pace due to new technology and reported cases are relatively small and based on individual case studies.

Morgan & Webster (2018) conclude that in cases of *confirmed* CAS, a referral to genetics should be considered since increasing evidence is showing that apraxia is a genetic disorder.

Another study in 2013 by Worthey, et al., concluded that whole exome sequencing (WES) supports genetic heterogeneity in childhood apraxia of speech. To clarify, since genetics was VERY confusing to me as a parent going through it, *whole exome sequencing is different* from a microarray and *different* from the standard genetic testing a pediatrician can order when screening for syndromes such as Down syndrome or Fragile X syndrome. A lot of parents have taken their child to get genetic testing with all results were negative, but the question remains—what was the child actually tested for? Tests for Fragile X syndrome and Down syndrome are like an aerial scan. These tests only look at chromosomes. Whole exome or partial exome testing are more finely ingrained, now zeroing in on the genes in each chromosome, like with a magnifying glass. These more refined tests are typically ordered through a genetics department that not only has a geneticist but also a genetics counselor. The rapidly developing technology in genetics means we will likely see many more genetic links to apraxia in the future.

In most cases, apraxia is a foreshadowing of additional neurological conditions to come. There are many, **many** combinations of co-occurring conditions that would be impossible to predict at that initial CAS diagnosis. There are *many* other conditions that can and *do* go with CAS. In very rare instances does a child keep *only* a diagnosis of childhood apraxia of speech.

CHAPTER 18

Advocacy

Stars.

Not as flashy as the sun,

duller than the moon,

They still light up the night sky.

The subject of poems,

gazed upon at night,

they are beautiful in their simplicity.

Metaphors for our children,

who shine bright on walk day.

I never set out to be an advocate or to be so actively involved in nonprofit work—but like with apraxia, advocacy work seemed to just find me.

I first heard about the Walk for Apraxia from Apraxia Kids the spring after Ashlynn was diagnosed. I signed up for it at the very last minute, holding the date for something "more important," not realizing at the time how life-changing the event would be.

The walk turned out to be nothing short of amazing. Ashlynn, along with all the other kids, received a medal, honoring her and all her hard work in speech therapy. While other kids play outside, kids with apraxia spend hours in speech therapy offices. No one sees all their hard work except for the therapist and the family. The medal ceremony felt like the one chance for our kids to be recognized for the stars they are. Ashlynn ran up to receive her medal, and as she returned to us, she had the biggest smile on her face. She may never win a medal for athleticism, oratory skills, or academics, but here she could earn a well-deserved medal for working hard to find her voice.

Fun activities before the walk made the day extra fun for everyone. There was breakfast, face painting, activity stations, and firefighters who gave tours of their firetruck and handed out free hats. After the walk, I was so excited about attending the next one the following year.

One day I was talking to Sharon Gretz (at the time, the executive director of Apraxia Kids), and she told me there wasn't going to be a Denver Walk for Apraxia the following year because the previous co-ordinators were stepping down. I was devastated. Ashlynn had only been to one, and it had been amazing to have a place to celebrate her achievements. She had worked so hard this past year and I was upset that she wasn't going to get any medals to reward her efforts anytime soon. I also thought of all my clients working just as hard. I decided I had to step up and take charge. I told myself that it didn't have to be a big event—a simple one to honor our kids would suffice.

I was already stretched super thin, working as an SLP at school during the day and then working nights and weekends building my private practice. I had no idea how I was going to find time to coordinate a walk, but I knew I was called to it. I had to do it.

I pitched it to my husband. He responded, "Are you crazy? When are you going to find time for that?" He wasn't being a jerk. He was speaking some serious truth. He knows me, and he knew I would want to devote all my time and energy to it; I never do anything halfway. So, many compromises later, I ended up being the Denver walk coordinator that year and every year since.

It's easy to make a walk happen. Set the date, secure the location, tell your people about it, sort the walk-day materials, and then have the event.

To make a large walk happen—and a walk I felt I could be proud of—took a lot more work. And, of course, every year I wanted it to be better and better. I wanted food options, entertainment, and fun for the whole family. I wanted the awards ceremony to be extra powerful and meaningful, so I added music. I wanted the day captured perfectly so I hired a photographer. I wanted the kids to have fun, so I added games and clowns and costumed characters. I didn't want anyone to be bored so I included lots of additional activities like bubble stations, coloring stations, sensory bead stations, and craft tables. I wanted to make more money for Apraxia Kids so I wanted a raffle table that would entice people to buy raffle tickets, with all proceeds going back to Apraxia Kids.

In the middle of all the planning, I became 100 percent committed to the nonprofit and its mission.

They kept their staff small and centralized to Pittsburgh, and relied on the help of walk volunteers around the country to raise funds. The reason for this was to maximize the amount of money raised going directly back into the community to help our kids via research, education for professionals, iPads, and grants for speech therapy, among others.

I knew I wanted to help them reach their goal. Apraxia Kids was life-changing for my family. The website had provided me information in the early days with my first apraxia client and then again when Ashlynn was diagnosed. I wanted to raise money for them so they could change more lives. I went from caring solely about honoring Ashlynn to trying to raise enough money to help every kid and family affected by apraxia in North America.

It was also easier to become invested as I started to get to know the staff at Apraxia Kids better. As a walk coordinator, I realized even more how this nonprofit was truly staffed with selfless people. They were there not for the money, but to help people.

I wish I had realized the importance of the walks and this organization at my first walk and worked harder to raise money. As walk coordinator, I have

organized fundraisers that only made fifty dollars, and yet, in my mind, we were still fifty dollars
closer to our goal. All donations and fundraising
efforts are necessary and so appreciated.

The walk was also my way to give back. Apraxia
Kids had helped my family tremendously in terms
of advice, training, advocacy, and even speech
therapy grants to help pay for Ashlynn's therapy.
Sometimes, paying someone back looks more like
paying it forward. It felt so good to be the light in
the darkness for families new to the diagnosis. It felt
great to see Ashlynn feel at home with her people.

Through the years, the walk has grown and in
Denver, we now have an entire team of walk co-
ordinators. Everyone has something valuable and
unique to contribute to make the walk special
for each child who attends. If you are new to the
apraxia diagnosis or even if you're not, I encourage
you to attend. You won't be disappointed. If you are
a professional who treats CAS, I also urge you to
attend; the support your clients will feel from you
will be immeasurable. I encourage you to go and
cheer them on. They may not get any other medals or awards while they are fighting to overcome
apraxia. This is their tournament game. Know how
important it is to them that you showed up, even if
they can't express it to you yet.

CHAPTER 19

Siblings

Little little baby Jace,
how I love your smiling face.
When the day is done and through,
I just want to be with you.
Little little baby Jace,
how I love your smiling face.
Chubby cheeks and curly hair,
Baby Jace, my snuggle bear.
Little little baby Jace,
how I love your smiling face.

Siblings, in general, will always have a certain rivalry. It's very common for siblings to fight and argue and drive their parents crazy. Siblings are always vying for their parents' attention and are frequently prone to jealousy. Any parent struggles to balance this, but when there is a child with special needs in the mix, it can feel like even more of a challenge. A child with special needs impacts the entire family, and siblings are no exception.

Apraxia can often run in families, but in our case, my daughter is the only one with apraxia, and her younger brother, Jace, is developing typically.

Jace is almost three years younger than Ashlynn. He was a challenging baby, who had difficulty with colic, reflux, and sleeping. However, sleep deprivation aside, I was never once worried about Jace's development, and that was a huge relief after our experiences with Ashlynn.

Jace said "Mama" with intention at eight months old. Ashlynn was working on saying it correctly in speech therapy at the same time, and he was able to belt it out without any issue. I felt so relieved that he crawled and walked on time. By the time Jace was a year old, he had so many words I was starting to lose count. With Ashlynn the opposite was true. She had so few words, I desperately kept track of any and all, including word approximations.

Somewhere along the way, though, my husband and I realized something. Amid our worry about Ashlynn and our daily struggles to help her master the simplest of daily living tasks, Jace was meeting and surpassing them daily. Of course, we were proud, but we had some unspoken agreement that we wouldn't praise Jace too loudly so as not to hurt our daughter. She had literally worked years and still couldn't master some things Jace could do easily.

It's hard to pinpoint the timing exactly, but when Jace was about two or three years old, I started to notice he was acting out much more. Yes, he was in the terrible twos/threes stage, but it seemed so much worse than the typical tantrums and acting out seen in kids of that age.

One night our kids were getting ready for bed. Ashlynn was struggling to put her pajamas on, while Jace had his on quickly. My husband then instructed him to put on his socks and Jace protested. He threw a tantrum and got in trouble, and the night ended on a bad note.

The next night found us again in the same scenario. Ashlynn was putting her undergarments on and missing the wrong leg hole. Meanwhile, Jace had quickly gotten his on. He was again instructed by my husband to put on his socks. He did, unlike the previous night without protest, and instead of praise, he was told, "Go and brush your teeth now." Then, like the night before, he threw a tantrum.

That's when it hit me. My poor little guy needed praise. If he were our first child, we would probably be posting social media updates on our prodigy and the newest thing he had learned.

But we weren't. So, scared to discourage Ashlynn, we remained silent. I knew something had to change. That night I talked to my husband and told him we never praise Jace. He regretfully admitted, "I expect more of him. I know he can do it. I don't have to worry about him."

I agreed, but I knew this was at the heart of the current problem. I repeated that he never praised Jace, and in that moment we both were solemn. "I don't want to hurt Ashlynn," my husband said.

I explained that in the process of preserving Ashlynn's feelings, we had hurt our son. All children want their parents to feel proud of them. Jace had consistently met our expectations and all we did with was give him more to do. The cards our daughter was dealt weren't fair, but it didn't mean our son had to suffer too.

Jace always had to tag along and wait while Ashlynn went to speech therapy, OT, and private swim lessons. As he grew into a toddler, he began protesting that he, too, wanted to go school, to speech, to OT, to swim lessons. The day we told Jace he could go to swim lessons if he pooped in the potty, he did so and kept saying over and over, "I pooped in the potty! Now I can go to swimming!"

I decided to start a sticker chart for both of them. Any time the kids did something that made me proud, according to their specific abilities, they earned a sticker. When they filled it up, they got a prize of their choice.

My husband and I started spending more time alone with Jace, without Ashlynn, so we could focus on him.

Even though we knew karate would be beneficial for Ashlynn, we decided to enroll only Jace. We wanted him to have something that was just his. He thrived in the environment and with the attention he received for his entire session.

Almost immediately, I saw a change in Jace. His face lit up when he heard he had made us proud. He kissed me more. When he was little, I used to say that he was my snuggle bear, and I now had my snuggle bear back. Interestingly, Ashlynn was *not* crushed, as I had feared. She cheered for him and celebrated his accomplishments. One night, they both declared at the dinner table, "We love each other."

One of the best sibling experiences came from a surprising place. I had heard about a special-needs camp in Colorado called Adam's Camp. It had great reviews, but it was very expensive since every child is with a skilled professional therapist all day. A client of mine mentioned that our local community centered board (CCB) would pay for it. Sure enough, they did, and the only cost to my family was for our lodging and the sibling camp.

It would be hard to say who received the most benefit from attending camp. Jace's sibling camp had all the same activities as Ashlynn's, plus some special ones like roller skating and go-karts. But it was more than just fun, it was also therapeutic. The kids had the opportunity to talk about their difficulties having a sibling with special needs in a group setting. The camp counselor, a certified teacher, said that due to Jace's young age, he hadn't contributed anything during group time, but he had definitely listened with intent to the other kids share their stories.

It's hard for little children to explain big emotions. Emotions like jealousy and neglect aren't always in their vocabulary. Their behavior is the most common and predictable way our children will show us what they are feeling inside. We can choose to ignore it, or we can decide to learn from it.

Every time my son has emotional outbursts, my husband and I now look at the source. Is he getting enough attention? Is he feeling neglected? Is he feeling invisible? Is he feeling unimportant? We don't have all the answers, but I do know we are trying our hardest to give him the childhood he deserves too.

Parenting doesn't come with an instruction manual. Maya Angelou once said, "When you know better, you do better." I can only hope our son will see some day that we failed, we learned, and we tried to do better from there.

CHAPTER 20

"If You're Happy and You Know It, Shout 'HOORAY'!"

You were assigned this mountain to show others it can be moved.
—Mel Robbins, inspirational speaker

At dinner the other night, Ashlynn was talking my ear off. In fact, she was talking so much, I had to remind her at least ten times that it's not polite to talk with food in her mouth. She kept talking while I cleaned up dinner and continued until she got ready for bed. Ashlynn didn't even want to stop talking to brush her teeth. Feeling frustrated, I told her to stop talking and brush her teeth. Then I paused.

Stop talking?

I remember that when Ashlynn couldn't talk, I told myself I would never, ever get mad at her for talking. I would never have guessed she would someday talk so much it would sometimes be annoying. Yet, years later, with the apraxia diagnosis far behind us, here I was telling her to do something else with her mouth. I smiled, thinking about how far we had come.

In the early days of Ashlynn's struggle with apraxia, I felt isolated, lonely, and fearful. I was that worried mom waking up each day and putting on a brave face but feeling crushed with the weight and responsibility of not knowing if I was doing everything I could or should to help my daughter but trying my hardest to figure it all out.

I remember cheering each triumph, no matter how small, and being filled with hope for a moment, before slipping back into fear and worry.

It seems like a lifetime ago. Ashlynn fought apraxia and won. She found her voice, and although her speech is not perfect, it is still a voice that everyone understands. I look at her and marvel at the fact that despite every negative prognosis that came her way in terms of additional comorbidities, she never gave up—or even considered giving up. She kept forging ahead, driven by her strong will and amazing resilience.

Many kids with apraxia do not have all her additional comorbidities. And yet, Ashlynn managed to beat apraxia.

I used to lament over the fact that my daughter was slammed with diagnosis after diagnosis. I was jealous of kids who *just* had apraxia and sensory processing disorder or who *just* had apraxia and dyspraxia. I felt terrible about it, but I was so scared for Ashlynn. Could she ever learn to talk with all these chips stacked against her? And if she learned to talk, would it be anything anyone could understand? I knew the stakes. The stakes were very high.

At some point though, as Ashlynn's apraxia started to resolve and I realized her clarity of speech was going to be fine, I would think back to my early questions: "Why me? Why her? Was this some cosmic joke that my daughter had all of these strikes against her and she was given to me, an SLP?"

Instead, I finally realized, Ashlynn was given to me so I could tell her story and offer hope to everyone else. Each new client I got that *just* had apraxia and one or two other comorbidities would ask me how my daughter was doing, and I could confidently tell them she was great. She had beat apraxia. I could offer them hope that despite overwhelming odds, she had triumphed. I started to feel proud.

Proud.

Ashlynn had significantly more obstacles to overcome, and yet she overcame them. Who better to provide hope to people than her story?

Last night Ashlynn begged me to sing "If You're Happy and You Know It" with her. It's one of her favorite songs. I'll be honest—I'm sick of it. But she was smiling at me and looking so hopeful, I didn't have the heart to say no. I started to sing but started fading out my voice. I soon realized she was singing the entire song on her own, with all the motor movements to match. This girl with apraxia had defied all the odds and could not only talk but could also sing. The last line of the song was so fitting for her journey.

"If you're happy and you know it shout, 'Hooray!'"

"HOORAY!"

RESOURCES

Nonfiction Books

- *Here's How to Treat Childhood Apraxia of Speech*, by Margaret Fish
- *The SLP's Guide to Treating Childhood Apraxia of Speech*, by David Hammer and Cari Ebert

Children's Books

- *Billy Gets Talking*, by Mehreen Kakwan
- *I Want to Be Your Friend*, by Angela Baublitz

Websites

- Apraxia-kids.org (previously CASANA):
  - Offers a growing library of on-demand webinars for professionals and parents.
  - Maintains a list of SLPs nationwide that have advanced training and expertise and are available for consult.
- ASHA.org:

- Offers a practice portal for childhood apraxia of speech.
- Includes a comprehensive technical report.

Funding

There are a variety of grant programs, community center board programs, and Medicaid programs that can help children who need additional therapy:

- United Health Care Children's Foundation
- Small Steps in Speech
- Scottish Right Foundation
- Easter Seals, Medicaid
- Katie Beckett Waiver
- Community-Centered Boards

BIBLIOGRAPHY

American Academy of Pediatrics, American College of Obstetricians and Gynecologists, & Committee on Obstetric Practice. (2006). "The Apgar Score." *Pediatrics, 117*(4), 1444–1447.

Anthony, J. L., Aghara, R. G., Dunkelberger, M. J., Anthony, T. I., Williams, J. M., & Zhang, Z. (2011). "What Factors Place Children with Speech Sound Disorders at Risk for Reading Problems?" *American Journal of Speech-Language Pathology, 20*(2), 146–160.

Baas, et al. (2016) "Examining Co-occurring Problems and Treatment Considerations in Childhood Apraxia of Speech." Presented at the American Speech/Language Hearing Association (ASHA) conference.

Bratten and Feolopolus, (2004). *Straight Talk about Psychological Testing for Kids.*

Camarata, Stephen, *Late-Talking Children: A Symptom or a Stage?*

Catts and Kamhi, (2005). *Language and Reading Disabilities, second edition.*

Caruso and Strand, (1999). *Clinical Management of Motor Speech Disorders in Children.*

Cooper-Kahn and Dietzel (2008). *A Parent's Guide to Helping Children with Executive Functioning.*

Duffy, Joseph (2005). *Motor Speech Disorders.*

Farinelli Allen, L., and Babin, E. A. (2012). "Associations Between Care-giving, Social Support, and Well-being Among Parents of Children with childhood apraxia of speech. *Health communication, 28*(6), 568–576.

Fernald, A. (1985). "Four-month-old Infants Prefer to Listen to Motherese." *Infant Behavior and Development, 8*(2), 181–195.

Fey, M. E., Cleave, P. L., Long, S. H., and Hughes, D. L. (1993). "Two Approaches to the Facilitation of Grammar in Children with Language Impairment: An Experimental Evaluation." *J Speech Hear Res*, 36(1), 141–157.

Gibbs, J., Appleton, J., and Appleton, R. (2007). "Dyspraxia or Developmental Coordination Disorder? Unravelling the Enigma." *Archives of Disease in Childhood*, *92*(6), 534–539.

Gerken, LouAnn, and Karla McGregor. "An overview of prosody and its role in normal and disordered child language." *American Journal of Speech-Language Pathology* 7.2 (1998): 38-48.

Hammer and Ebert, 2018. The SLP's Guide to Treating Apraxia

Hanford, E. (2017, September 11). "How American Schools are Failing Kids with Dyslexia."

Haynes and Pindzola (2004). *Diagnosis and Evaluation in Speech Pathology*

Kranowitz, 2005. *The Out-Of-Sync Child.*

Lewis, B. A., Freebairn, L. A., Hansen, A. J., Iyengar, S. K., and Taylor, H. G. (2004). "School-age Follow-up of Children with Childhood Apraxia of Speech. *Language, Speech, and Hearing Services in Schools*, *35*(2), 122–140.

Lyon, G. R., Shaywitz, S. E., & Shaywitz, B. A. (2003). "A Definition of Dyslexia." *Annals of Dyslexia, 53*(1), 1–14.

Maas, E., Gildersleeve-Neumann, C. E., Jakielski, K. J., & Stoeckel, R. (2014). "Motor-Based Intervention Protocols in Treatment of childhood apraxia of speech Curr Dev Dis Rep, 1 (3).

Maas, E., Robin, D. A., Hula, S. N. A., Freedman, S. E., Wulf, G., Ballard, K. J., and Schmidt, R. A. (2008). "Principles of Motor Learning in Treatment of Motor Speech Disorders." *American Journal of Speech-Language Pathology, 17*(3), 277–298.

Meyer, Susan (2004). *Survival Guide for the Beginning Speech-Language Clinician.*

Miron, C. (2012). "The Parent Experience: When a Child Is Diagnosed with Childhood Apraxia of Speech." *Communication Disorders Quarterly, 33*(2), 96–110.

Murray, E., McCabe, P., and Ballard, K., (2014). "A Systematic Review of Treatment Outcomes for Children," *American Journal of Speech-Language Pathology*, Vol. 23, 486–504.

Murray, E., Thomas, D., and McKechnie, J. (2019). "Comorbid Morphological Disorder Apparent in Some Children Aged 4–5 Years with childhood apraxia of speech: Findings from Standardised Testing." *Clinical Linguistics & Phonetics, 33* (1–2), 42-59.

Rosenbaum, P., and Stewart, D. (2004, March). "The World Health Organization International Classification of Functioning, Disability, and Health: A Model to Guide Clinical Thinking, Practice and Research in the Field of Cerebral Palsy." *Seminars in Pediatric Neurology* (Vol. 11, No. 1, pp. 5–10). WB Saunders.

Roth and Worthington (2001). *Treatment Resource Manual for Speech-Pathology, second edition.*

Strand, E. (2017). "Appraising Apraxia: When a Speech-Sound Disorder Is Severe, How Do You Know If It's Childhood Apraxia of Speech?" *The ASHA Leader, 22* (3), 50–58.

Strand, E. A., and Debertine, P. (2000). "The Efficacy of Integral Stimulation Intervention with Developmental Apraxia of Speech." *Journal of Medical Speech-Language Pathology, 8* (4), 295–300.

Made in the USA
Monee, IL
04 February 2020

21314017R00097